HOPE *to* COPE

KATHERINE DOLPHIN GRIFFIN

Illustrated by Mia and Colin Griffin

KATHERINE GRIFFIN
KATHERINE DOLPHIN GRIFFIN
PUBLISHING

Published by Katherine Dolphin Griffin Publishing 2022

ISBN: 978-1-3999-0199-4

Instagram @my.hope.to.cope.story
Facebook: Katherine Griffin
Email: myhopetocopebook@gmail.com
Website: www.hope-to-cope.com

Printed and bound in Ireland by
www.printmybook.com

This book is dedicated to anyone who hasn't been heard yet, and in particular, my dad in heaven who listened and heard me always.

Bless you. Thank you x

'Owning our own story and loving ourselves through that process, is the bravest thing that we will ever do.'

Brené Brown

'People talk about caterpillars becoming butterflies as though they just go into a cocoon, slap on wings, and are good to go. Caterpillars have to dissolve into a disgusting pile of goo to become butterflies. So if you're a mess wrapped up in a blanket right now, keep going.'

Eileen Hopkins, Jennifer Wright,
@ehopkinstherapycoach.

Foreword

Meeting Katherine Dolphin Griffin was like recognising instantly a good friend in this world, a warrior and survivor who carried love in both her presence and words.

I was one of the first people that Katherine told of her desire to share her stories in a book. It led to the question, was it her desire? The reality was that everyone who had been touched by one of Katherine's stories over the years had told her to write a book! After spending an hour together and hearing some of her stories I felt the same. Thankfully so did she and she stepped into a remarkable new journey bringing Hope to Cope to life.

The author's focus and desire for this book has always been that others can learn from her journey or find some recognition in another, that they will know someone else understands their difficulty or pain in a sometimes unfair life. When faced with struggle including cancer, chronic illness and eventually the terminal illness of her beloved Dad, Joe, Katherine shares how she coped and I trust that we can all find hope in both her words and her experience.

In our first meeting, and in watching the journey of this book over nine months during 2021, I often heard Katherine talk about her Dad and I was both touched and impressed at the relationship that father and daughter shared. It is in many of the relationships carried within this book that Katherine shows us the essential truth of life, so beautifully captured by Rumi; 'We can only learn to love by loving.'

It is in her choices to constantly look for hope and ways to cope that Katherine gifts the reader the acknowledgement of deep pain and traumatic life events alongside the potential for a new perspective.

Hope to Cope is essential reading for anyone on life's journey, it is a gift to all those in the trenches and a pathway to gifting your soul a warm hug. This is not a story of seeing the good in spite of circumstances. It is a story of living through the circumstances, of accepting that sometimes coping is enough and overall one of great hope. Katherine shows us through her own life stories that in accepting what we cannot change we can look to the things that we can change, and put our focus there.

Heather Shields
Ireland, December 2021

Heather Shields Publishing
Co-Founder The Self-Publishing Network

Contents

Introduction

I was diagnosed with thyroid cancer in December 2012. I was 37 years old, my daughter was 8 and my son was 4. My dad had cancer 5 times. He didn't survive the fifth round. He died on world cancer day, February 4th 2017, having battled tremendously for 9 years.

He died because the drug he needed didn't launch until it was too late for him. I have unfinished business with cancer and I am on a mission to help make more survivors by fundraising for Cancer research in his honour. I am proud to be a survivor.

I am fundraising in a way that is giving all of me, in an honest, raw and passionate way. I wanted to put as much of myself into it as possible, so I decided to write a book which shares my coping strategies that have resulted in my healing and recovery from trauma. I hope that my feel good story of finding ways to cope with life's challenges will help others too.

I love to read and write, doing so helps me to understand life's challenges and discover solutions. Writing gives me ownership of a problem as it takes it out of my head and onto paper. It supports me to see all the facts and look at the evidence.

Through various struggles in my life, I was unable to find what I was looking for in a book or find someone who has suffered in a similar way who could help me or advise me. I was left to teach myself various coping strategies over the years through invention or rather by learning through experience. I am very conscious that this might be the case for many people. I believe that it's important to share ones learnings so that they may help someone else who may be on a similar journey or who is a little lost right now. Once you have suffered you don't want others to suffer too.

I am a wife and mum of two, a primary school teacher, an only daughter and I have four brothers. From my earliest memory I was a daddy's girl. When we were teenagers, our mother left home. I was the only female left in a house of 5 males. My relationship with my dad and brothers changed. It had to. Our lives had changed.

I took on the role of 'woman of the house,' endearingly referred to as 'the boss' by my dad and brothers. We got on with it and life was good. We grew up, got jobs, entered relationships and had kids. I absolutely love my brothers. They mean the world to me. There is nothing they could do to make me love them less.

In Feb 2008, when I was six months pregnant with my second child, dad was diagnosed with Non-Hodgkin's Lymphoma. In 2016 dad was diagnosed a fourth time but this time it was back on the double. He had a tumour in his throat and one in his stomach. The one in his throat was treatable but the one in his stomach was not. It wasn't possible to operate as the tumour was too close to vital organs and there wasn't a drug available to treat it either. However, there was one coming online in October. It was now March.

Dad was told to put his affairs in order, a day I will remember always as the beginning of the end of us, our team. We began to hope and pray that he would survive long enough to get the trial drug. He did, however, cancer had a firm grip on him at that point, the side effects of the drug were too great and he grew gravely ill. He went into hospital on January 3rd for his immune booster treatment which he had been receiving every three weeks since his bone marrow transplant. Unfortunately, he caught the vomiting bug. He had nothing left to give. I brought him to Marymount Hospital and Hospice on Jan 16th where he died on February 4th 2017, World

Cancer Day. The lowest day of my life.

I don't want my dad's memory to die or with it the story of this beautiful man who was deeply driven, intelligent, charismatic, warm and strong. I learned a lot from him and I am who I am today because of him. This is his story too. The only time that I was unable to support my dad was when he grew gravely ill and needed to go to Marymount. I struggled deeply with handing him over. It felt similar to that feeling when your child heads off to school for the first time. You realise that you are not needed in the same way as before.

There isn't just one reason why I wrote this book but rather several. I primarily wanted to share my story of love and determination. I wanted to show how love really can conquer all. There are no special powers when it comes to dealing with challenges because strength will come. It comes every time. With every challenge that comes our way we learn new skills that will help us with future challenges. A type of resilience building. I am going to tell my story and share my learnings from taking a pragmatic approach to life. I hope that they will help you to find your path if you are a little off-course right now.

While this book has been painfully difficult to write, I have found great healing while doing so. I am reminded of the journey, all the achievements and grievances and of the very special people that I have in my life. I have challenged myself through facing my demons and letting go of pain. I learned many new skills along the way. There are wonderful people in the world who want to help and that has been humbling to see.

It has been twelve months since I had surgery or a new diagnosis. That is a celebration for me and I am looking forward to the next chapter in my life. I now have a positive thing to celebrate in February 2022 with the launch of this book, which will ease the pain.

It has been a month that I have hated since cancer came knocking first. My hope is that my honesty and pragmatic approach will help you to identify with and relate to my story and instil in you, hope to cope.

The book includes 16 stories or essays, each of which begins with a motivational quote. Each essay tells a story of a challenge or struggle that I experienced in my life. I tell what happened and the tools I used to overcome each challenge. I talk about what I have learned about myself and others and what learnings I will be taking forward with me. Each story can be read as its own entity. At the end of each story there is a notes page which readers can use to write thoughts that were provoked while reading, or a list of things they want to do, or change, or to write lines that resonated with them. Or write feelings and emotions or whatever one likes.

The book mark with the serenity prayer will guide the reader along through the journey of self-discovery. Wishing you the serenity to accept the things that you cannot change, hope to find courage to change the things you can change and the wisdom to know the difference.

It has been quite liberating to turn a negative into a positive and to succeed over a challenge. I am trying to have a good life, to follow my dreams and to be a good role model for my children. I refuse to let challenges stop me or to hold me back from achieving that. I have never suffered from depression but having experienced the loneliness, sadness and despair that comes with grief, I can now identify with depression a little more. I have struggled at times. I think that a lot of people can identify with that feeling following the months of living with Covid.

Dealing with life's challenges doesn't have to be the end of the world as long as you have hope in your heart. Hope to cope. Nothing lasts forever, not even the bad stuff. *This too shall pass.* Hold firm and do what is right for you. Do the next right thing. There is always hope. Try to remember to mind yourself in it all.

Good luck.

'Live, Love, laugh, and hold hope in your heart.'

Hugs & positive vibes,
Katherine

Story 1: Home Sweet Home

'Sometimes I feel lost,' said the boy.
'Me too,' said the Mole, 'but we love you, and love brings you home.
I think everyone is just trying to get home,' said the Mole.'

The Boy, the Mole, the Fox, and the Horse. Charlie Mackesy.

The things that teach us most in life are our experiences. Home is where our first learnings take place, and all our future experiences are grounded. Our parents are our first role models.

When I was 16 years old, my mother left home and never returned. That left me home alone, in a male house that consisted of my Dad and four brothers. That part of my life set me up for my life ahead in so many ways. I often refer to my teenage years as being the best years of my life. I was able to call upon my strengths to run the family home, help rear my brothers and get an education, a strength that I didn't realise that I had. I have drawn on this strength so many times since.

I am the second eldest in my family. We lived in the country, which was very peaceful and ordinary in the 1980s and early 1990s. My Dad worked with the Department of Agriculture, and he also ran his own business. My mother was a full-time mother. She was a fabulous nurse back in the 1960s. She loved her job. She gave this up when she married my Dad. My father was from Galway and my mother is from Offaly. Dad was transferred by The Department of Agriculture to Cork in the 1970s.

The 1980s were a great decade to grow up in. In the 80s in Ireland, though there was mass unemployment, mass immigration and political turmoil, everyone lived a simple life, and everyone knew and got on well with each other. The 80s was the decade that gave us the Rubix cube, the Lolo ball, Care Bears, Gameboy, Cabbage Patch Kids and my little pony. It saw the introduction of neon legwarmers, and power dressing for women with shoulder pads and ladies trouser suits inspired by Sue Ellen from Dallas. HB ice-cream was the ultimate treat, in particular the Fat Frog, the Freaky Foot with the chocolate toe and the wibbly wobbly wonder. It was a time before internet or mobile phones, instead payphones were dotted along the footpaths. Televisions had two channels with programming that didn't start until 4pm in the winter and 5pm in the summer. If you wanted to change the channel, you had to get up and do it manually. There was no pausing the television to make a cup of tea or to pop to the loo. Popular T.V. shows included, Bosco, Dempsey's Den with Zig and Zag, Fraggle Rock, The Muppet show, MacGyver, Cheers, The A-Team, Knight Rider, Happy Days, Mork and Mindy and the Simpsons to name a few. The Walkman was the coolest thing to own and making mixed tapes was the original Spotify playlist. In order to record your favourite song from the radio, you pressed down hard on the play and record button simultaneously. There were no food deliveries. Eating out was something of a novelty for many – an event to mark a special occasion such as a christening or communion. I remember going to the Island Gate Restaurant in Glounthaune for my communion dinner. In our house just the communion child got to go to the restaurant with my parents as it was too expensive to bring the whole family. The other children were minded by neighbours or *other family members. The 80s were a time when your parents rarely knew where you were. We were pretty wild as children, we were into everything, and we loved the outdoors. We stayed outside until it was time to eat. The minute we came home from school, we went out to the woods, our cabby house, and the fields. We loved the freedom. This type of freedom isn't often offered to young children today because it isn't considered safe.*

When our mother left home, we got even more freedom, as you can imagine. Mam left one random Sunday morning; we were just teenagers at the time, and it was a massive scare for us. This was the first time I experienced trauma. Mam did not leave a note and so was reported as a missing person. The guards came to our home. They tapped the phone. Three days later, mam called to tell us that she decided to leave and would not be returning. Though I adored my father, I was acutely aware of his lack of experience in running a home.

Our mother was a typical eighties mum, and her day revolved around the kids and the house. She rarely did anything for herself. However, she was a great cook and baker and an avid gardener. Our house was a great home, and we loved it.

We began our journey in our new family unit without our mother, a challenge we had to face because we had no choice. I took on the running of the household, and everyone helped out. There was only one dinner that I knew how to cook, the one-pot wonder stew, so we ate that every day for a year. Unlike nowadays, there was no access to the Internet, so if you didn't know something and didn't have anyone to ask, you did without, simple as that. In a way, I think that ignorance was bliss. It was liberating.

There were lots of teething problems as expected. However, we muddled along and got on with it all. We had a great little setup at home. We were happy. There was no fuss, and we all pretty much did whatever we liked. We knew that we had each other's back, and it all worked. I did most of the cleaning and cooking, which is why I did most of the giving out.

Back then, tidiness was not something that my brothers shared with me. They couldn't be more opposite if they tried. Clothes were everywhere. The shower was blocked and there was constantly pee on the toilet seat and the floor. The boys were never bothered by this, but it drove me crazy. I used to get notions of trying to reign them in. I would bag up all their clothes and throw them out the back door. They found this hilarious. They would laugh and say, 'the sister's lost the plot.' Then, we'd all laugh about it and move on again.

Every Saturday morning, Dad and I would go down to the local shop. We would do the shopping for the week. That was probably the only day that we had food in the house. The weekly shop would have to be 'topped up' several times during the week. We got our meat from our local butchers. The lads loved meat. I would make big stews, and they would lap it up. They were great eaters, and it was a pleasure to feed them. They ate whatever was put in front of them. We would often have other mouths at the table as our house was like a drop-in centre at the time.

You were sure to find laughter and mischief in our house. It was a very open house, and everyone was welcome. I loved that about home. I loved our home - not just the people in it but the actual house itself and everything in it.

Maur, my then-boyfriend and now-husband, often laughs when he speaks about one of the first encounters with life in my home. He remembers an afternoon when we had returned from a drive. I had gone to the bathroom and returned to the kitchen like a madwoman.

I was giving out about the state of the toilet. I was very cross. I went to the fridge to get a tomato to make a sandwich. Someone had turned up the temperature in the fridge and froze everything in it. Maurice said I threw the tomato at the door, which it hit with a loud bang and dented. I declared, *'this is a fecking tomato.'* It was frozen solid.

I hated that he never got the lovely motherly welcome that one would like a boyfriend and future husband to get. Whenever I went to his house, his mother would make tea and cake. She always checked if I had dinner or if I would like a sandwich. Maurice said that it never bothered him. He loved my home, and he enjoyed the craic and the relaxed atmosphere. Home is where my heart is, and our hearts were undoubtedly there.

There is a bright side to most things. Maurice never had to worry about impressing the mother-in-law. He was accepted as one of us from day one. My younger brothers loved that he had a car and could drive them about the place. I couldn't drive, so he was like a hero to them.

We might have come from a 'broken home', but there was nothing broken about us. We were very close as siblings and never gave our father an ounce of trouble outside of the typical teenage stuff. We all worked hard and became self-sufficient adults. But most importantly, we were happy and healthy. In many ways, we looked after each other like a small team because we had to.

We were all in the same boat, and we wanted to stay together as a family. So in a way, my mother having left home, and my parents' separation and divorce brought us closer as siblings and made us stronger people. At a young age, we had to learn what patience, empathy, teamwork, and sacrifice looked like, and it did us more good than harm.

I would relate my home experience to the job's skill set at

each job interview I attended. For example, I explained how I could motivate a team by referring to examples of encouraging the boys and Dad to tidy as they went - to use the washing machine or wear dirty clothes, to cook or go hungry. I had learned these leadership skills as a teenager at home.

I explained that the best way to motivate was to realise that everyone has a price. We are all inspired by something, and you have to teach people how to treat you.

If I did everything for the boys, they would never learn to be self-sufficient, nor would they respect me. I learned many management skills at home. Not just because my Dad had a business at our doorstep but because we ran our house like a business, and we were all stakeholders and shareholders. Everybody had a role to play.

My parents were legally separated for several years before they could get a divorce in Ireland. A tough time for us all. My eldest brother was in Germany on college placement at the time. I was studying in the United Kingdom, and Dad was at home with my three younger brothers.

I would fly back and forth between the UK and Ireland to attend court hearings. I loved and respected both my parents. I was your typical daddy's girl. We were great friends. We became best friends.

I don't think that my parents were ready for marriage. But back in 1973, if you got pregnant, you got married. So thankfully, their union produced our family.

In my opinion, my father and mother were not a good match. They were brilliant people but far from brilliant together. They were very different and had had very different upbringings.

My mother was probably looking for a 'hands-on' family man. My Dad loved his family, but he left the running of the house entirely with my mother. That was the norm back then. He was a knowledgeable man who loved to be busy, and he had his finger in many pies. He was a great provider but was probably too busy to be a husband. I remember my mom being sad and lonely. She cried a lot. One day she decided that she had had enough. She left home and never returned. While divorce was the finality of my family, it didn't heal my parents' relationship. We never again spoke of her leaving and their subsequent divorce. We survived the divorce of our parents. We all settled into our lives. That pain was behind us, and we all moved on.

Several years later, my Dad's death completely uprooted our lives and changed our family dynamic forever. I saw my Dad every day, some days, several times. He was my first call in the morning at ten to eight, on my way to work, and my last call at night before I went to bed. He used to get cross when I called him on my way to work. He said that I woke him every morning at ten to eight with my panicking. When Dad was dying in Marymount, his alarm went off on his phone at eleven minutes to eight in the morning. I realised that I never woke him, he was always expecting my call. He didn't want me to feel that I needed to call him and didn't want any fuss, but more than anything, he never wanted to be a burden.

I didn't sleep until the light went off in his studio. We were next-door neighbours, so the glow of his office, or studio as he called it, shone into my bedroom ensuite. I could see his head in the studio window whenever I went to my clothesline. I could see his red jumper in the studio window when I drove past his house. We ate together every day. We hugged every day. I went home every day. Now, I don't go home anymore.

Because I came from a 'broken home', I put a lot of pressure on myself as a young woman to get a good education, a good job, and a career. It is terrific to be highly motivated, but I had an unhealthy set of expectations that stemmed from my mother leaving home and my parents' divorce. It steered the course of my life in many ways.

I was highly motivated to have a job to support my children if my husband left me. This was my thought process in my late teens. But, unfortunately, this was my fear, and I had to have a plan and a backup plan.

This fear was in vain because I was fortunate with every job I had. I have worked with the nicest people. I am also lucky with my husband. We are very close. He is a fantastic husband, father, and friend. He was an amazing son-in-law to my Dad and is a brother-in-law who one can always be relied upon.

No matter how much planning you do for the life you want and lead, life can still throw you curveballs. Mine was my cancer.

My children are the new generation with parents who are more aware of their spiritual, emotional, physical, and psychological needs. Our parents did the best they could with their information, education, mental and emotional maturity. There is no blame or resentment.

There was no play therapy for my brothers or me when our mother left home. You just swallowed the drama or locked it away and got on with it. I have learned, the hard way, that you can't control it all. You just have to do your best along the way while respecting and listening to yourself. You know you best.

I felt like a hamster on a wheel, not knowing what I needed for a long time. Now I try to listen carefully to myself. I listen to what my mood is telling me, what sparks joy, and what takes pleasure from me. When I know how I feel and what is causing those feelings, I have a better shot at coping with daily life.

When I was diagnosed with thyroid cancer, my children were

8 and 4 years old. I spent my entire time putting things in place for them for when I would be in hospital and later when I would undergo radioactive iodine treatment in an isolation unit. I desperately tried to make this journey as easy as possible on them.

Every family has its challenges, and we were no different. I thought about everything that went through my head all those years earlier when my mother left home. *'Who will cook, clean, buy our clothes, bring us to and from school?'* I needed to work out who would do these things now for my children.

Maur was great with them, but he had to work too. I also wanted to support them emotionally. That was when I discovered the fabulous Cork ARK, cancer support group. They gave me invaluable support and guidance. They helped me to deal with my demons.

I had to face the feelings of my youth which had been locked away for decades. I asked myself, *'How do I leave my kids for surgery and treatment, and how do I get through 6 weeks of no contact and 2 meters apart after radioactive iodine treatment?'* I had never left them before.

That was hard, but you know what, we underestimate children all the time. I realised that when they have the information, they have the power. They know that they are loved. They knew that I hated leaving them and that I would be back as soon as I could, and it was not by choice but by the circumstance that I was going to be separated from them temporarily.

They still have scars, of course. It was a scary time, and you can't protect them from everything. They heard a lot. They saw a lot. I put the two of them into play therapy so that they could heal safely and healthily. Similar to adults, children struggle too. However, the most significant stress of my illness was how it would affect my children emotionally.

Children typically don't edit their thoughts before they speak. I remember my daughter telling me that she saw her Dad as the 'strong' one. He is strong. There is no doubt, he is strong, and so am I. But though it hurt that she didn't see me as strong anymore, she didn't mean it. What she meant was that she viewed health as strength. So it was my challenge to show her that strength comes in many forms.

Emotional strength was a strength that we all had to practice and learn very quickly. I spoke about the strength of mind and body that is required to fight an illness. But, to be honest, only time could teach that. She needed hard evidence, which she got as I grew better. But it did take a long time for her to see me as a 'strong' person again. I remember listening to a conversation she had with her play therapist, and she said she was afraid that her mother would die, so she felt as though she had to get used to not needing her.

That statement hit me like a tonne of bricks. It ripped through my heart and broke it. I was immediately back in 1992 with all the feelings of my mam leaving home. She didn't mean it or understand what she was saying. She was just expressing how she was feeling. She was feeling real fear—a threat to her family unit, her security.

For me, that was the most expensive cost of cancer—the emotional damage. I will be forever grateful that I have had the years to rectify this, and we have completely rebuilt our relationship. We are as close as we were before cancer knocked, if not closer.

I'm humbled to have survived to hear her say things like 'Mam, you are my everything about everything.' *I have learned that communication is vital. I tried to be as honest as I could with the children. That's hard because your instinct can be to shelter and protect them from hurt, but in my experience, it's best to talk to them* and explain as best you can about what's going on. They are not stupid. They will sense tension and fear like a fox senses its prey.

I realised that they tried to work it out for themselves when I didn't talk about what was going on. They read between the lines and got a scary version of what was happening.

I remember not telling the children when Granddad moved to Marymount Hospital and Hospice to receive palliative care. I just carried on like he was in hospital. Then, one day my son asked me if Grandad was dying because he was in Marymount. I wondered how he knew that Grandad was in Marymount. He simply said that he heard somebody asking me on the phone, and then he put the word 'Mary' and the letter 'M' into Google and looked it up. I was dumbfounded. He was eight years old.

Kids need to learn skills to manage their emotions healthily. It's essential to teach them coping skills to help them face their fears, calm themselves down, and cheer themselves up. Coping skills increase resilience because they help people appropriately handle negative emotions, panic attacks, and other difficult situations. When you effectively deal with a negative emotion or problem, you also move on and let go of the negative feelings associated with that experience.

Life can be so cruel. It really can. If you get sick, it is not your fault, but I felt real deep-rooted guilt for bringing it to my house, husband, and children.

I honestly never felt scared of getting cancer or thought that someone else should have gotten it above me, but I felt hard done when it came to my door when I was a young mother studying and caring for my Dad with cancer. That was tough because it was a lot of juggling. It was a lot of pain.

I believe that you never know what you are truly capable of until you ride a challenge, arrive out the other side and look back at *what you have achieved.*

It's as a result of thinking about it or writing it down that you give yourself a little tap on the back and smile at how wonderful you can be. All of us have that capacity. It is a marvellous skill. So as I write today, I am thinking of all the achievements, big and small, even the tiny ones.

My current challenge is to go back home someday. I will do it, and I will be so proud of myself, but I'm not there yet, and that's ok too. I have looked in my Dad's bedroom window, and that's a start.

I have learned to be gentle with myself until I can achieve the new things on my list. I will keep an eye on all that I have ticked off. That will give me strength and confidence moving forward in life. I have brought real positives, resilience, and learnings from my childhood home to my forever home.

I can draw upon the lessons of joy and the importance of communication and love. Had I not experienced trauma in my home as a teenager, I don't think I could have anticipated the trauma of my cancer on my children and consequently take a pragmatic approach in protecting them.

Education is an admirable thing, but it is well to remember from time to time that nothing that is worth knowing can be taught.'

- Oscar Wilde

Thoughts provoked from reading each story (explained)

'Butterflies show us how we can go within ourselves to dissolve old forms and morph, rebuilding and evolving ourselves, they show us the importance of surrender and trust as part of the essential process of growth and renewal.'

Anna Cariad-Barrett Eco therapist and co-author of Sacred Medicine of Bee, Butterfly, Earthworm, and Spider.

I always find that when I read a book, I tend to write notes over the printed words and turn down 'dogs ears' on the pages and stick post-it notes all over books. I decided that when I wrote this book I would include a thoughts provoking page at the end of every story so that you can doodle and take something away from each story.

Words: Words or messages that you liked and that may help you.
Feelings: What feelings did these words give rise to?
Actions: What will you do? What do you need to do?
Timeframe: When will you do this?

Thoughts provoked from reading this story

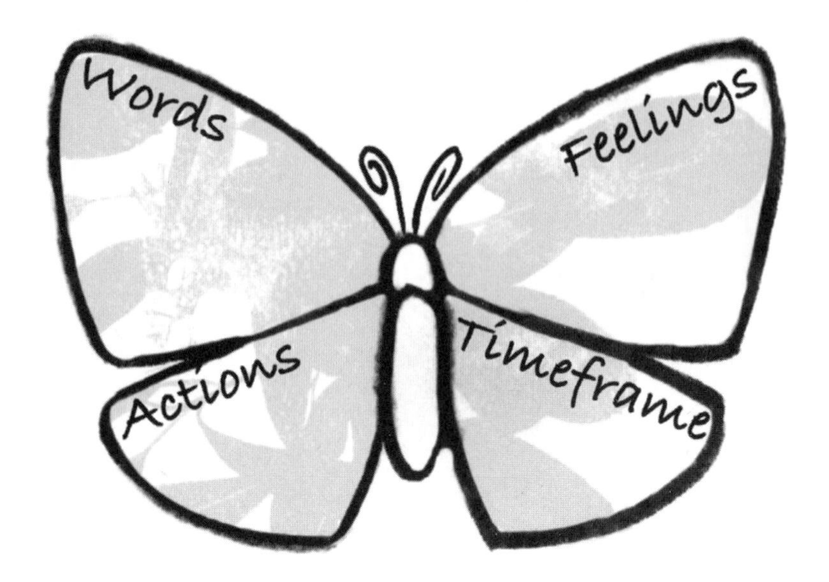

Notes:

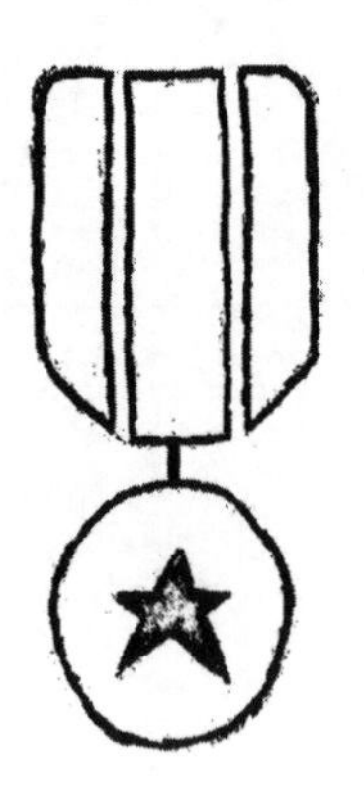

Story 2: Nothing to fear, but fear itself.

'Change is the law of life. And those who only look to the past or present are certain to miss the future.'

J.F. Kennedy

Life is constantly changing, and it can be challenging at times. Embracing change can help us to succeed in life and to cope better with it. Unfortunately, however, change can sometimes cause fear.

It's a vicious circle because one can hold back from achieving one's full potential when one is afraid. It's worth remembering that fear is a natural emotion. It is essential to recognise it and to cope with it as best as one can. Fear can give an adrenaline rush, and it can sometimes cause complications in our lives.

When it came to the time for me to go to college, I decided that I wanted to study business and tourism. The most suitable college for this was in Birmingham, England. I wasn't afraid of traveling to England at 18, quite the opposite. I love to travel. My challenge was making it work and balancing college in England with home in Ireland. Dad would never ask me to stay at home and sacrifice my career. But I needed to find a way whereby I could cope with both. It would be a considerable change.

I decided not to look too far into the future. I looked far

enough to apply for my course. I was accepted and I applied for a student loan which got approved. Dad paid for my flight and gave me some money to tide me over until I got a part-time job. Because of my young age, I was allowed to stay in the college hostel, which was fantastic news. I felt safe there, and I immediately got a college family, which made settling in and coping much easier. I loved it. My course went well, and I made great friends.

I phoned home every night and caught up with my Dad and two younger brothers, who were now both in secondary school. I would help them with their homework and issue some instructions regarding the running of the house until I got home. After that, I went home as often as I could. Flights were very cheap at the time. Dad paid for my flights, and I would help him out with the household chores as much as possible. Towards the end of the first year, I had to go home a lot because my parents' divorce case had come up, and I had to appear in court.

I am glad that I embraced the opportunity to study in the UK. There were so many benefits of that change in my life. It gave me a college education, lots of friends, happy memories, independence, freedom, responsibility, and most importantly, the clear message that I can do anything I set my mind to.

An example of a change that I embraced, but was not completely happy with and still beat myself up about, was my attempt to run my Dad's company after he died. A week before he died, Dad decided to retire from his company. He wanted to shut it down. I told him that I would keep it going and at least honour the work booked. It put a smile on his face, and I'm sure it took some pressure off him.

Honestly, I don't know what I was thinking, I was afraid, but it gave him hope to cope. I will never forget or regret that. I would do anything for him. I hadn't a clue about videography, however, thankfully, Dad had a friend who knew the ropes, so he did all the video work and editing. That left me with the bookings, stock, packaging, bills, deliveries, and accounts. The main challenges I faced were juggling this with working full time, being a wife and mother, and being crippled with grief. I embraced it because I gave Dad my word. I balanced it all for months, and then I had to accept that it was time to close my Dad's company.

That was the second time that I had to let go of him, and I struggled greatly with that. I felt that I had failed my Dad. My inner voice was screaming all sorts of negative remarks my way.

I went back to counselling so that I could see the wood from the trees. While it wasn't a change that I enjoyed or felt proud of, I cannot regret it. I must instead look at the facts. Dad had one less thing to worry about as he faced his death. He would understand that this wasn't the career for me. I know that I did my best, and so does he. I faced my fears. I had honoured all his booked work, paid all the bills, shut the company down properly with his accountant, and messaged his suppliers and customers. That had to be good enough for me because it was the best of me. I now had to face living with the absence of both Dad and his business next door. I learned an awful lot about myself through that process.

Embracing change helps us develop as human beings, change can be fearful, but fear is reasonable. After we ride the waves of change, we can look back and either be happy with the change or learn from it. You can't lose if approached in the right way. Be fearful but challenge it because change is inevitable. You will find yourself moving from judgement to journey. On this journey, you will discover skills you didn't know you had. You realise how strong you are, and you see your worth. You gain knowledge and experience and meet wonderful people along the way.

You must embrace and accept change if you want to follow your dreams and live your best life without fear stopping you and missing out on the best things in life.

Change can be transformational and make us better by walking away from difficult people and difficult situations in our lives. It can give us back our freedom. Change can be a positive thing because it can help us develop resilience and provide us with many opportunities. Sometimes you have to cope with change to cope with life.

If only we could stop, review, and embrace change instead of doing the same thing and getting the same results or expecting different results.

'The price of doing the same old thing is far higher than the price of change.'

Bill Clinton

Then, we would be so much happier and more successful in life. Therefore, whenever I am facing a potential change in my life, I ask myself five questions.

1. What's the worst that can happen?
2. Whose problem is it?
3. Have I evidenced that I have managed change in the past?
4. Who could help me?
5. What's the next best thing that I can do?

If the answer to question one is anything but death, I tend to go for it and embrace the change, even if it is with gritted teeth. Coping with grief has made me braver. It has taught me that life is short, and that gives me the confidence to live my life. Question two is an interesting one because sometimes, part of the change is someone else's problem. You can't fix everything. I already know that the answer to question three is yes. I just added that I need to see things in front of me, I'm a visual learner, especially when panicking. Question four is about compiling a list of suitable people who could help. Question five is about focussing on the here and now. What can I do now? What must I do first? One step at a time. Rome wasn't built in a day. The mountain gets smaller with every bucket of soil that you remove from it.

There is an old saying that a change is as good as a rest. What I always notice is that nothing is ever as hard as it first appears. I used to often reply no to an invitation. I would talk myself out of all the reasons why I should go. However, a couple of years ago, I decided to say yes to every invitation for a whole month. Then I tried it for six weeks. I was blown away by the difference that this made in my life. I didn't regret a single choice.

Next, I took it a step further, and I gave out some invites and organised some get-togethers. After that, I started to live again, and I found it very healing. I know that I must live my life and have a good life; it's what my Dad would want for me. It's what I want for my children. I needed to do this in my own time and in my own way.

Everyone's journey is different, we must each respect that. This is your life, live it your way. Everyone who loves you wants the best for you. Likewise, you want the best for everyone that you love. Remember, life is precious. Live it.

This sentiment reminds me of the poem 'Epitaph,' written by contemporary writer Merrit Malloy that I first heard on NCIS and found the full poem thanks to a post by David Joyce on Facebook. I encourage you to look it up and share a short snippet below.

"Epitaph captures how our loved ones can best keep our essence alive after death, not merely through reminiscence but through purposeful acts of love" - (Upworthy.com)

Excerpt from Epitaph

You can love me most
By letting hands touch hands,
By letting bodies touch bodies,
And by letting go of children
That need to be free.

Love doesn't die,
People do.
So, when all that's left of me is love,
Give me away.

- ***Merrit Malloy, 1985***

Thoughts provoked from reading this story

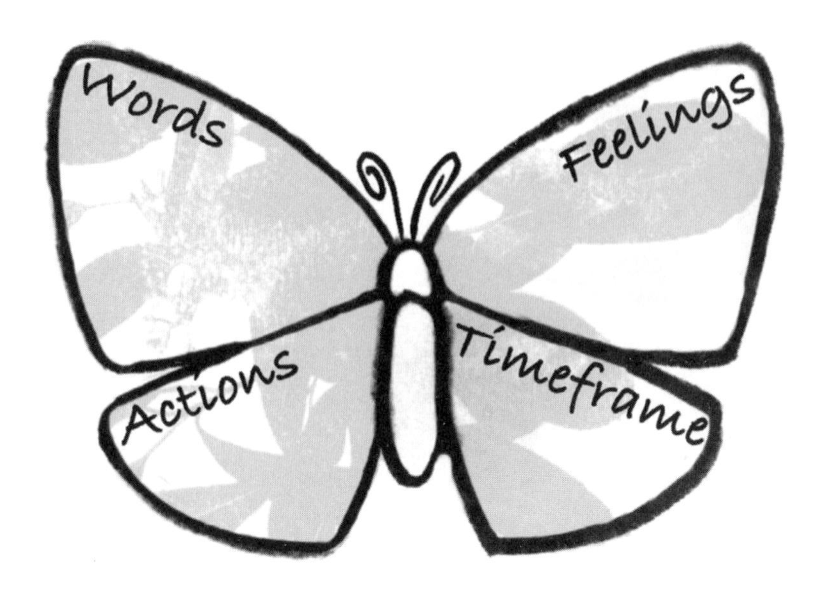

Notes:

Story 3: Help!

'You just do it. You force yourself to get up, you force yourself to put one foot in front of the other, and God damn it, you refuse to let it get to you. You fight. You cry. You curse. Then you go about the business of living. That's how I've done it. There's no other way.'

Elizabeth Taylor

Your past is your past. You cannot change your past, but you can learn from it. You can change your present and your future. You will need help along the way, so be prepared to ask for it.

The first significant change in my life was when my mother left home. She was a great mother. She was your typical Irish mammy. I would never in a million years have thought that she would 'give up and go'. I knew that she was unhappy. I could see that. But I always saw her as being strong and able to cope. Then, when I grew up, I began to understand how she was feeling and began to accept why she did what she did.

As an adult, I accept her decision to leave because she could not stay any longer. She did what was suitable for her. She showed self-love. I wish I knew then what I know now. If only she would have been able to explain her thought process and her decision to us back then so that we had a chance to try to understand it.

I always felt that she fell out of love with us or gave up loving us. But, in truth, she had given up feeling unhappy and was lost in herself. That is why I believe so strongly in the power of communication. I also think that when bad things happen, you can make good things happen too. But, unfortunately, sometimes you have to wait a long time to see that some things happen for a reason.

My mams departure brought a massive change to our house — both from a practical point of view and an emotional one. That was tough, and it was sad. Mam dropped me off at my part-time babysitting job, and she went from there. I have thought about that day so many times over the years. I carried guilt because, at the time, I didn't notice anything suspicious. It was crazy for a few months until we got into a routine and began to accept our new normal. This was what our family looked like now, and we had no choice but to get on with it.

Like most challenging situations in life, you can underestimate your ability to cope. But, fortunately, coping tends to come when you try to survive. It's like firefighting. You ease yourself into the burning building, one step at a time, and quench the fire that's in front of you, and you continue with that until there is no fire left except for the burning ashes.

That's where therapy comes in. Unfortunately, nobody spoke about or recommended therapy for my brothers or me back in the early nineties. We received lots of sympathy but no empathy. As a result, we suffered a massive trauma in our lives, and we were just left to get on with it and muddle through as best we could. We had to grow up far too quickly. We accepted that this was just our tough luck and got over it, but you never get over things like that unless you address them and deal with them.

I always felt that they would creep up and bite me at some stage. Unbeknownst to myself, I was mapping out my life so that I would get a good education, get a great job, work hard and earn lots of money so that I could be secure on my own. If I was lucky enough to meet someone and have kids, then I needed to be able to rear them on my own if that need be. I was always expecting people to leave me, which was a tremendous amount of pressure on my shoulders.

I knew that I was very driven but didn't realise what the driving force was. I discovered this force when I was diagnosed with cancer. My medical team advised me to seek guidance on articulating the situation to my children and preparing myself mentally for isolation and treatment. I went to Cork ARC. Cork ARC offers support for people with cancer and their families. Services include physical therapies, professional counselling, and practical information to reduce the distressing impact that cancer can have. I was unprepared for all the sadness that would come out of me in therapy.

I was terrified that my children would think that I would leave them. I was very stressed and upset to think that they would be disadvantaged or hurt in any way by my illness. My eldest was getting her communion in a few months, and all I could think about was her big day. My son was starting Montessori, and I needed to be there for him at drop-off and collections. It was my plan. I couldn't accept this change of plan on any level. So I continued to fight it.

What I needed was to find a way to cope. I went for several therapy sessions to help me understand and accept what had happened to me as a child and accept that it was not my fault. I learned and acknowledged that my circumstances were very different from those of my mother. I was different from my mother, and I had learned a lot from my parents' experiences.

Therapy was a place where my therapist validated my feelings, and there was no judgment. It was a safe place where I could be myself. I could iron out my feelings and talk through my anxieties. I always felt that I wore the label of a deserted or lost child. Finally, I began to put the pieces of my life's puzzle back together. I started to recall mannerisms and strategies of my younger years. I rediscovered all the occasions in my past whereby I used the technique of pretend. I pretended that I was happy to be going home for Christmas like my college friends. I was to a point, but it was a different homecoming for me. I didn't drop my bag of laundry in the hall and sit down to a home-cooked meal. Instead, I had to catch up on all the deep cleaning that had built up since my previous trip home.

I was jealous when I visited Maurice's family, they had a lovely cosy house. His mother always had a lovely dinner ready and was so welcoming. I would have loved that treatment for Maurice in my home. However, he didn't mind and said that he loved my house for different reasons. We had made a happy home, but there was always a sense of the maternal absence.

I am forever grateful that I went for therapy. It is something that I may never have done if it wasn't for me trying to protect my children from pain. I never realised that I had buried pain. It always amazed me that if I needed a tooth pulled, I would go to a dentist. If I needed an antibiotic, I would go to my doctor but never felt that I needed to mind my mind in the same way. We need to normalise therapy.

I am glad that I went to therapy. I strongly recommend it if you have been through a difficult time or are trying to cope with a challenging change in your life. If you need help, ask for help. A therapist will be more objective than your friends and family. They are qualified to best support your emotional needs.

I went back to therapy when I learned that my Dad would die. I knew that I needed support because I couldn't cope with or accept him leaving me. I struggled.

Dad didn't want anyone to know that he was dying, and that was a burden that was difficult to carry alone. I wasn't as strong as he thought, and that was ok too.

Strength, in my opinion, is doing the strong thing. So I did the brave thing, I asked for help, and I went and got help. I later also got therapy support for my profound grief. As a result, I put boundaries in place, took responsibility, communicated clearly with my loved ones, and found peace.

Minding yourself amid change is crucial. You will find the strength that you need, and you will find the way. Be like a flower, survive the rain but use it to grow. Be kind to yourself and those around you. It costs nothing, and everyone benefits.

Change is an inevitable part of life. However, some changes can be easier to face and to handle than others. Some changes can be optimistic once you decide to take a leap of faith. Some can be excruciatingly difficult, but each brings a sense of achievement and pride once you've walked through it.

There is no doubt that change can cause stress. However, I find that stress comes from over analysing the decision at hand. A decision that I was terrified of making but glad I embraced was my trip to Dubai in 2018 with my girlfriends. I have never taken a holiday without my children. To be honest, the only time that I was away from them was for surgery. This realisation was the logic that I used when deciding if I should go to Dubai or not. It's strange, I was saying no to a break with my friends after the trauma of the previous ten years, in particular the previous year, where I had to watch my Dad grow weaker and weaker and die. I was mentally and physically exhausted. If I had to go into hospital for a week, I would have done it, and they would have been fine — crazy logic.

Going to Dubai was the best thing that I did at that time. Finally, I turned a corner with my grief. I got a break from the constant reminders that my Dad was dead. I laughed for the first time in over a year. I had 'me time' for the first time in 10 years, it was just what the doctor had ordered. Laughter is a great tonic. My friends knew that I needed help and support. There is always someone out there who can help and support you to cope.

A change that I found excruciatingly challenging was coping with and recovering from my father's death. I will be, forever, a different version of myself because of that journey. When you lose something you can't replace, what do you do? I felt as though I was running frantically in my head.

A tsunami or tidal wave, also known as a seismic sea wave, is a series of waves in a water body caused by the displacement of a large volume of water, generally in an ocean or a large lake. - Wikipedia

Tsunamis are ranked among the world's most destructive forces. - Britanica.com

Much like when a rock plunges into a still pond, once a tsunami-generating disturbance in the waters occurs, a train of outward-propagating waves comes from the disturbances central point.

Grief, to me, is comparable to the destruction of a Tsunami. It rips the land apart, and it rips your world apart, making it unrecognisable. When a Tsunami hits, like grief hits, we retract into ourselves. We go indoors until it is safe to venture out again. Then, while bracing ourselves, we take a look outside to assess the damage. Still unable to do anything, we begin to process it all. We walk through the damaged environment pushing debris out of our way, all the while gathering salvageable items. Then it's time to rebuild your life, a new life, never to be the same, similar to a new home after a Tsunami.

A Tsunami was described earlier as a displacement of water. Likewise, grief is a displacement of the heart. Displacement, by definition, is the difference between the initial position of something and any later position. When you are lost, nothing looks familiar. Everything is out of position.

What we also find is that with pain comes strength. When you lose something you can't replace you find something you need that you never knew you had. You never really know how strong, smart, or brave you are until you see evidence of it in yourself.

My advice to you is to remember this evidence. If you think that you will forget. Write it down. - *I survived cancer. I survived the death of my beloved father. I survived studying with two small children, and I survived the radioactive isolation room.* This list can, and probably should be as long as possible and/or necessary.

Challenge yourself to put one achievement onto this list per month. List your accomplishments. *I stood up for myself by ... I let go .... I gave up trying to ...... I am starting to ....I've stopped doing.... I want to ....*

You will find a new you, one that can and will cope with your new world.

I do feel that you lose it all for a while. The journey with the new self, commences at the beginning or, more precisely, at the end of the old life.

The challenge is to continue to move forward.- one foot in front of the other, baby steps. If it's Black and white, why colour it? It can be difficult. Be honest with your feelings. Name your feelings. If you're angry, say you're angry. I loved the way that Disney portrayed feelings in the movie 'inside out.'

My Dad referred to the analogy of the green grass quite often. The grass may look greener on the other side. Look and learn but don't obsess. Nobody knows what goes on in another's patch, and we all stem from different foundations. To know all is to understand all. So do your best with your own grass.

Ask yourself what are you going to do with what you have? Have you gratitude for what you have? Should we do a stocktake of the things that we are grateful for? Should it be a daily, weekly, or monthly stocktake? There are so many things that cause anger and sadness. But there are also so many things to be grateful for. Make a list.

We grow and change to survive in our new world. We are like butterflies.

When I knew that Dad was going to die, I felt utterly overwhelmed. I didn't know how I was going to accept it. How could I best support Dad and find the strength to keep going myself. How do you let go of someone you love so deeply? How can you function while that's going on? But you know, you do, I don't know how or what happens, but something happens. You just find strength out of love. You just get the power to move forward. The strength and hope to cope.

I knew that I was struggling and needed to reach out to a counsellor about three months before my Dad died. I needed help accepting that my Dad was dying and nothing that I would do would save him. I was devastated. I had only been to counselling once before with Cork ARC. This was in advance of going into isolation for my radioactive iodine treatment, to manage my children's questions and anxieties around my treatment, and learn various strategies to cope with the separation that it would cause. They were fantastic. A network of support is vital. Reach out. Ask for help.

I was given Catherina's name by a friend who assured me that I would like her. That was important to me. Connections are essential to me. I want to make connections and be relaxed and comfortable around the people in my company. If I was going to pour my heart out and lay myself bare, I needed someone who could connect with me very early on. I didn't know what to expect or what to say. What I did know was that I needed help, and I couldn't face this alone. I have a great circle of friends and family, but I needed professional help. I needed to put my best foot forward and support my Dad in the best way that I could. It had to be about him, and he couldn't see me break.

With every challenge that I have faced, the universe has gifted me with a great person. For example, when I was in school and dressed like the fifth son, I was blessed by my friend Fionnuala who became like a sister to me. When I left home to study in the UK, I was given Helena. She was in a similar situation to me in that her mum had died when she was young, so she was the woman of the house in her home, just like me.

When I started my first big job, I was gifted my friend Marie. Then, when my son Colin had rubella, and I was retraining to be a teacher, the universe gave me Deirdre. When I started my new career as a teacher, I was given Kay. When my Dad was on his cancer journey, I was given Ger. When my Dad died, I was given my friend Tara. I have lots of special people in my life. My favourite is my husband, Maur.

When I sat in front of Catherina, and she asked me why I had come to her. I told her that I couldn't accept that my Dad is dying. I couldn't believe that I heard myself say those words. There was particular healing in hearing myself say those terrible words. We spoke for two hours. I started at the beginning. I needed Catherina to know the whole story and the full extent of what she would be helping me to survive. It wasn't just a father-daughter relationship. We were best friends with a fantastic connection and a deep love. I was not just losing my Dad, I was losing several people in my Dad.

Catherina listened with an open heart and an open mind. We laughed, and she had an incredible way of relaxing me into my thoughts and fears and supported me just to say how I was feeling. I adored the fact that now and then, she would throw out a few swear words. It just brought a sense of normality to an utterly abnormal time.

I hadn't been for counselling when my parents separated or divorced. I suppose Dad was always my counsellor. It's ok to need help. We all need help from time to time. At the end of my first session, it was apparent that I had a long journey ahead of me. I knew that everything I hadn't dealt with in the past would come crashing down. Similar to when you open the wardrobe that's full to the brim, everything comes tumbling out. I had to address my past so that I could tackle the present and face my future. So week after week, we chipped away at my thoughts and fears. I cried a lot. I discovered a lot. I knew that I would never be the same again, and that was ok. I didn't expect to be the same. My love and my loss were too deep. One thing I knew for sure, I needed to fight for my kids' sake. I had to become strong again.

When the life you live and love changes, you change too. You have to, to survive. You are looking out at the world from a broken heart. Everything looks and feels different. You have to learn to navigate through it, and it is difficult.

There should be a rule book for grief. Or at the very least a set of guidelines. And I don't mean for the grieving, but rather everyone around the grieving. Some people tiptoe around the grieving, other people stay away from the grieving, and some just assume that you are strong enough to cope alone or that someone else is looking after you. Grief is, in my opinion, the most significant trauma in life. People are afraid of grief. Grief is the price you pay for love. Ask the grieving person what they need, don't assume that you know what they need. Everyone's grief is different. For me, I just wanted people to sit with me and listen. I wish that speaking about and dealing with the challenges of death and loss could be normalised. I feel that there is massive pressure on the grieving to get on with it and get over it long before we are able.

Imagine if we each wrote a list of all the challenges we have faced in the past decade, we would be surprised. We would be surprised by both its length and of our successes. Of course, we face challenges all the time. But, they typically come with firsts. First child, first time driving. The first day at a new job, first date, first day at school for our children, first time experiencing grief.

When I look back at the various challenges I have faced, I am happy with what I achieved. The only one that I still struggle with a little is my grief. I want not to cry when I think of my Dad. I want to accept that he is no longer with me. But, the truth is I am frustrated and angry. I want him back. So, every day I wrote about how I was feeling that day. I noted the things which brought me joy, sadness, anxiety, happiness. Then, I looked for ways to manage these feelings and the situations which caused them. I found that doing daily journaling or as I call it, daily analysis, really helped me to cope.

Looking back at successes also gave me strength and confidence. You need discipline and consistency. If you stop, then start again, that's ok. Remember, it's your journey because it's your life. Do it your way, one step at a time. Know when to go and when to slow. Sometimes doing nothing at all is what you should be doing.

I find this very difficult because I think I must be doing something or going somewhere all the time. However, I have learned and accepted that this was pretty much because I didn't want to be alone with myself. I didn't want to be quiet with myself because I wasn't able to hear my thoughts. They were too painful and raw.

I am much better now. I still have challenging days, but not like before. Time has helped me. Asking for help has helped me. I am more mindful now, and I am conscious of being mindful versus having a mind full. I try to look to the future. To see what today's actions will look like when I get to cash them in, motivates me. I try to have hope. Hope is always there.

My advice to you is this, ask for help. Help comes in many forms - neighbours, friends, family, work colleagues, counsellors, play therapists. Your past does not define you. Your future is waiting for you, for your choices, and your actions. As Walt Disney said, *'if you dream it, you can do it.'* Worry is a prayer for what you don't want to happen. Worry will not change the situation. Action will. Make that plan and embrace your future today. Carpe Diem!

Thoughts provoked from reading this story

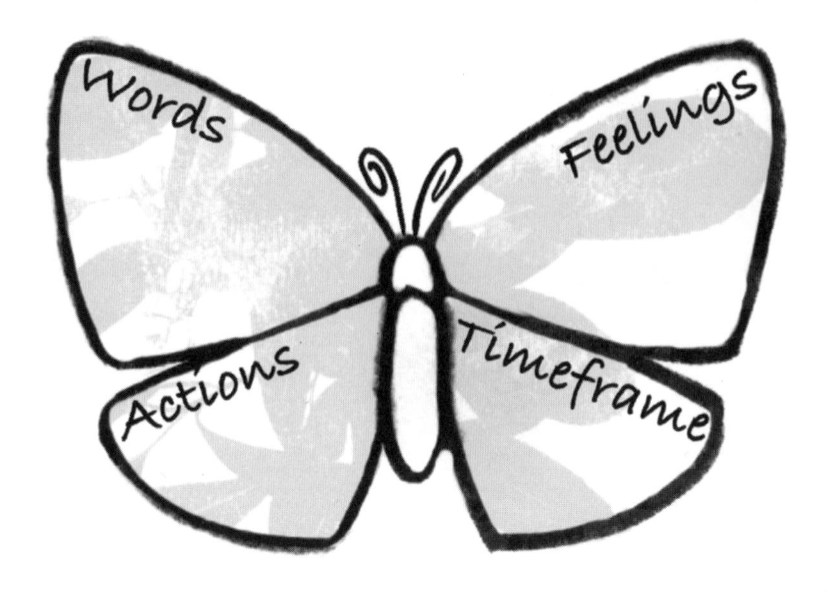

Notes:

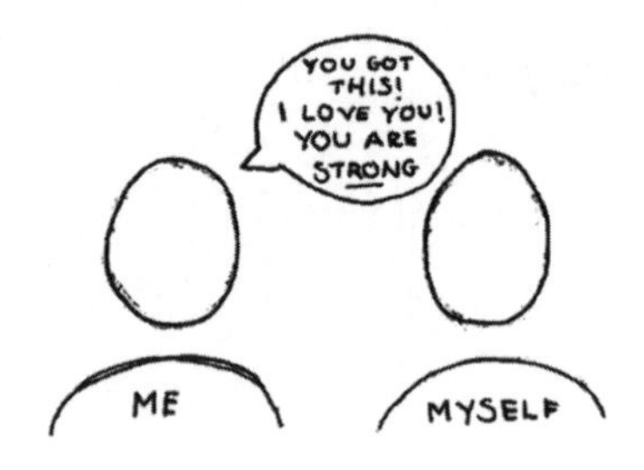
YOU GOT THIS! I LOVE YOU! YOU ARE STRONG
ME
MYSELF

Story 4: Change Our Words, Change Our Mindset

'Words have energy and power and the ability to help,
to heal, to hinder, to hurt, to harm,
to humiliate, and to humble.'

Yehunda Berg

Have you ever thought about how you speak to yourself? What is that inner voice in your head saying to you? I could not believe what I heard myself say when I listened to my inner voice. Why, when I speak nicely to everyone I meet, is my inner voice such a real bitch sometimes?

When I sit, she's reminding me of all the jobs I have to do. When I want to skip my walk because I'm tired or don't have the time, she calls me a lazy bitch and accuses me of making excuses. When I want to buy something as a treat, she reminds me of the bills I must pay. When I want to wear something different, she tells me that I'm mutton dressed as a lamb. When I want to, and need to say no, she reminds me of the people I will be disappointing and how negatively they will speak of me. When I want to try something new, she highlights that my cup is already full.

When I want to tell someone to leave me alone, she threatens me with no friends. When I want to say how I feel, she reminds me that I need to toughen up. When I need to take a day off work because

I am unwell or exhausted, she tells me that I'll be thought less of at work. When I want to ask for help, she tells me to be independent.

So how do we quieten our inner voice? Or at least teach her to be kind? Self-criticism is not good for us. It's poisonous. You must ask yourself if you would use that tone with your friends or family.

'Kind words can be short and easy to speak,
but the echoes are truly endless.'

Mother Teresa

THINK. How do you offer love to yourself just as you offer it to your partner, friends, children? Trust what you know about yourself, not what others think of you. Set an intention for yourself. *What do you want to change or improve? Ask yourself if you are struggling and why?* We can form opinions of ourselves based on previous experiences. It is normal for people to struggle and to suffer. *Ask yourself what you need right now. Do you need a break, more affection, etc.? Acknowledge how you are feeling. Ask yourself what do you need to help you feel better?* Find that support. Tell yourself that it will all be ok and offer yourself kindness.

Suppose you go back and think of yourself as a child. Think about how you looked. *What was your personality like? What things did you like to do then?* Tell your inner child/ inner voice something that you like about her. Hug her. Think about how you speak to yourself versus how you would talk to that child if she were standing before you. Think about this child all week when you are speaking to yourself. First, notice and acknowledge what she is saying, then tell her to stop hurting you. If she is looking for attention and appears worried, tell her that it's alright, you are safe now.

I got into a spiral of waiting for the next bad thing to happen, trapped in a negative mindset. I understood why it happened, but it wasn't good for me or my health. We must try to stick to the facts. Facts and not opinions, insecurities or fears. What is the evidence? Imagine Judge Judy standing in front of you. *What would she say? Ask yourself what do you like about yourself?* Tell yourself daily what you want for yourself.

Therapy helped me to see the bigger picture. I was suffering from analysis paralysis because I was over analysing everything. Learning coping strategies along the way has helped me. Now when I face a decision, I ask questions like *'who's problem is this?'* If it's my problem, then I'll try to sort it, but if it's not my problem, I will walk away and leave it. I can't fix everything. It's not my responsibility either. I can only try to fix what's mine to fix. I will always try to be kind.

Words are expressed thoughts. We should be careful with our words to others and, most importantly, to ourselves. The way that we speak to ourselves can be a game-changer. It costs nothing to be kind, and you gain so much.

One of my favourite proverbs is the French proverb *To understand everything is to forgive everything.* We never know what is going on in someone else's life or their head. If we knew everything that was going on for everyone, we might be a little kinder. We are not all excellent at expressing ourselves or reaching out and communicating with those around us about how we feel. We are also not great at communicating with ourselves properly. Nor do we always show self-compassion. Therefore, it is imperative to be conscious of our inner voice and our inner critic.

Do you speak to yourself in the same way that you talk to others? What's the difference? Are you kinder to others? Ask yourself how often am I critical of myself? Be curious and open to your inner critic. Practice positive talk and real talk, and go easy on yourself.

When I was doing many interviews in my twenties, I would write positive things about myself to help myself get a good job. I was always surprised by my list, and I noticed that I could see how much it improved over time. The more that I tried, the more optimistic I felt. I continued to keep a 'praise book' over the years in which I would write all my positive affirmations, any compliments or pieces of praise that I received. I also put photos in my 'praise book,' all the pictures that made me happy. I do something similar in my kitchen. I surround the walls above my kitchen table with photos of the people and places that I love.

When I was in Eircom, we did a 360-degree feedback session. It involved having to fill out a questionnaire, and my colleagues were also involved. Each person gave the other person feedback. We do something similar in school with our two stars and a wish strategy whereby we offer two pieces of positive feedback and one part for improvement. It was like a praise sandwich with the input in the middle and the positive affirmations on either side. '*I liked your writing today. Do you think you could include more paragraphs tomorrow because that would make your fabulous story come to life?*'

I also recommend a mood board consisting of 3 to 4 things that you like about yourself, lovely cards you have received, beautiful pictures, pictures of items you would like to own or accomplish — positive quotes and affirmations. You could also consider keeping a positive daily journal to reflect on whenever you have a bad day. Keep a small one in your handbag or under your pillow so that you can have positive messages and pictures at hand to support you. I do something similar in school. A positive news board – e.g. *pupil X has moved up a reading level.*

If you struggle to think of positive things to say about yourself, then ask friends and family. When trying this out with kids I would suggest that you scaffold it for them. Make a game out of it. '*If I were a ...... I would .... because I......*'
Make loops of this game by giving them a category such as – *'if I were an animal, car, colour, food, place. Cartoon character, I would ... because I ....'*

When my husband and I were going out first, we would ask each other, *'do you love me today?'* And we would each answer in a cute way like, *'so far, so good today.'* As the years went by, we had shortened the question to one word '*TODAY?*' Our kids asked us what we were talking about one day, so we explained. Then they started to do it too. Now, they are both teenagers and hate being embarrassed by their parents saying, '*I love you*'. So instead, we just say '*TODAY?*' and a simple nod will suffice. It is communicating in a way that's both supportive and comfortable for everyone.

Therapy helps identify habits that we are doing that are not beneficial to us. I have received invaluable support this way. I have learned so much about how I think and how I have felt for years. I realised that if I changed my voice, I could change my mindset. So I started to change how I speak to myself, and it has had such a positive effect on my quality of life.

I've often suffered from imposter syndrome.
'*Imposter syndrome (IS) refers to an internal experience of believing that you are not as competent as others perceive you to be. While this definition is usually narrowly applied to intelligence and achievement, it links perfectionism and the social context.*' - verywellmind.com

When I got my first real job as a sales representative with Eircom, I worked very hard and loved my job. I found it relatively easy and enjoyable. I worked with some fantastic people, some of whom are still my friends today. I exceeded all sales targets set for me and quickly climbed the ladder within the company.

Each time that I experienced success, I suffered from imposter syndrome. I felt that I was a fake, that I didn't deserve to be there. I attributed my success to good luck. My sales approach was my invention based on honesty, passion and being myself. I chatted to all my customers and my team as though we were all good friends and the chat was very relaxed as a result. There was nothing wrong with this approach, and it worked. It was very successful. *Why then was I so hard on myself? Why couldn't I accept that this was something that I was good at?*

I felt the same imposter syndrome when I retrained as a teacher, only this time, I thought that I had more reason to feel that way because I was a late starter.

I remember a mother at my school asking me why teaching was an afterthought, a late in life decision. I nearly died. I had put so much work and sacrifice into becoming a teacher and I was good at it. I took this one parent seriously. The lady probably didn't mean any harm. She was just surprised when I told her that I was only teaching a year at the time. Maybe it was her way of complimenting my achievement. I will never know because I instantly thought the worst. Deep down, I must have been feeling insecure about my new role. It was difficult because I had such success in my previous job, and then I had to start at the bottom again. A bit like how a first-year student feels moving from being top dog in primary school to becoming small fish in a big pond in secondary school.

I feel that same imposter syndrome creeping back up as I write this book. But I'm sticking to the facts and being honest. I am using the 'Judge Judy' approach of looking at and sticking to the evidence. I am not trying to patronise anyone. I'm certainly not up on my high horse or know it all, far from it. I'm just a regular girl highlighting what I learned, and hoping that maybe that will help someone else. Perhaps it won't help anyone. Perhaps I'll be gifting books for Christmases to come. I'm also not claiming to be a good writer. But I know for sure that I love it, and I'm also so proud of myself for trusting myself and pushing on with it. Again, I take the pragmatic approach. If it doesn't work, it doesn't work, but I'll have tried. It's better to have tried and failed than to have never tried at all. I might even surprise myself. I know that I'll die happy if I follow my dreams.

I will now share an example of a time when I conquered my fears while using my voice to raise awareness of cancer.

Vhi Healthcare Testimonial Advert - changing my mindset and being brave

In October 2016, dad's medical team put him on a trial drug called Ibrutinib. It was his only chance to survive cancer a fifth time, his last chance.

Ibrutinib, sold under the brand name Imbruvica among others, is a small molecule drug that inhibits B-cell proliferation and survival by irreversibly binding the protein Bruton's tyrosine kinase. Blocking BTK inhibits the B-cell receptor pathway, which is often aberrantly active in B-cell cancers.

It is not a chemotherapy drug but one of what is termed 'targeted therapy.' Target therapy results from years of research dedicated to understanding the differences between cancer cells and normal cells according to Chemocare.com

The drug was costly, but, fortunately for dad, he was covered by Vhi Healthcare. The Vhi Healthcare advert is spot on with their message, '*when you need us, we're there.*' They were there for my dad, and they were always there for me.

I spent a lot of time on the phone with Vhi Healthcare. They provided cover for this particular drug and the necessary approvals without delay, and cover was put in place immediately.

One day, while on a call with Vhi Healthcare, the lovely agent remarked on my story of dad and me and our cancer journey together. We chatted about the beautiful Vhi Healthcare testimonial adverts with real stories.

Later that evening, I told dad what the lady from the Vhi Healthcare had said to me, and he was all ears. I was surprised by his interest because he is a below-the-radar sort of guy. Quietly confident and unassuming.

Five months later, a month after dad's death, which some people refer to as a 'month's mind', I got a call from Vhi Healthcare. I thought they were calling about dad's policy which I had phoned to cancel a few weeks previously.

That's a big challenge with grief. It is cancelling policies, salaries, subscriptions, direct debits, and standard orders. It's like cancelling someone's life which, in a way, is what you have to do. It is excruciatingly difficult.

It was painful to see the 'late Joe Dolphin' written. He was never late. It was numbing to think of him in the past tense. It will always be difficult not to see him again. I miss his hugs and smile most. I had to split my head into two mindsets. One where I was cancelling his life and the other whereby I kept him alive by running his business.

Vhi Healthcare reminded me of my application five months earlier and asked if I was still interested in telling my story. I explained that I was not in a good place because my dad had just died. The *lady on the phone accepted that. She was very compassionate, and we continued to chat for nearly an hour. She was warm and friendly, and I found great comfort in my conversation with her. She listened and then complimented the lovely bond that I shared with my dad.*

I spoke to dad's friend, Ger, and she thought there was nothing to lose by meeting with Vhi Healthcare. A month later, Ger and I went to Dublin. The interview was at a recording studio because the testimonies are stories as the storyteller tells them. They are honest, genuine stories.

When I got to the reception, I got cold feet. Then I noticed a dolphin trophy on the counter. I thought it was a lovely sign. My dad's surname is Dolphin.

Dad was with me, at my side every step of the way. There was a radio on the counter. The dolphin was sitting upon it. Dad wanted to buy me the same radio on our last shopping trip to Cork in December 2016. So I hung onto these heavenly messages, and I carried on.

When I entered the waiting area, I noticed a bowl of love heart sweets on the table. My heart could have burst open at that point. Love hearts were a trendy treat at weddings, dad used to video up to 5 per week, and he always brought me home the love hearts.

I knew, when I saw them that day, he was with me and supporting me. So I opened a packet and written on the first sweet were the words 'go for it'. I had a lump in my throat. He was shining down on me in all his glory.

I went into the recording studio, and I met a lovely lady who would interview me. Outside the screen sat a team of marketing people. We spoke for nearly two hours, and then I left. A couple of months later, they said that they would like to use my story as a testimonial and asked me to send some pictures of myself and my family.

Another couple of months passed, and I received a call one day inviting me to Dublin. I received an email that showed the running of the 'shoot day' and a storyboard. I felt like a movie star. They certainly made me feel like a celebrity, checking what I liked to eat and drink and what I wanted to wear.

I told them that I love dresses, which I do. Well, I adore dresses. They have always been my armour. Dad said that I was always prancing around in a dress when I was little, and it didn't stop me from climbing a tree or being part of the gang of boys.

I remember when I was a little girl, about four years old. I heard the doorbell ring. The bell was constantly ringing in our house, our house was a kind of halfway house, and we loved it. We all ran to the door as usual. The man at the door said, '*God, that's a fine crop of boys you have Joe, you have your little team in the making.*' I remember looking down at my dungarees and stamping my foot. '*I'm not a boy,*' I declared to all.

I liked dresses at that age, but I didn't have many as it made more sense financially to wear my brothers' hand-me-downs. But I can tell you that was the day that I officially fell in love with dresses.

My neighbour was very handy with a sewing machine, and she made me several dresses. My mother was part of the Irish Countrywomen's Association (ICA), so some of her friends would often send a box of clothes my way. To be honest, those boxes of clothes were the highlight of my childhood.

To this day, clothes still have a positive effect on my mood. I love to get dressed up even if I'm staying at home. I love all things girly. I adore shopping. I feel the internal scars and war wounds when I look in the mirror, but my clothes cover that. I see that my clothes make me look good, and hence I feel good.

Vhi Healthcare sent me a beautiful pink and white Ted Baker

dress in the post. It arrived at my door in the signature Ted Baker green box. I floated to my room and was hysterical with excitement. I rang Dublin to say that I had received it. They informed me that it was my TV dress.

I got my date for filming. When I say filming, I mean just interacting with the props. There was no acting involved. Thank God.

I travelled to Dublin with my friend Fionnuala. She has a clothes shop and goes to Dublin regularly to meet with reps so we went into the city and spent hours in Brown Thomas. I got my makeup done and bought a dress. A Sandro dress, which is my favourite brand. That Sandro dress is still my favourite dress today.

I mark every occasion by buying a dress. Every dress has a meaning and a story. We bought ice cream and went into St Stephen's Green Park and sat chatting in the sun. It was a beautiful day.

It was the first day in as long as I could remember when I did something for myself. It was wonderful. We checked in at our hotel and went through our purchases while drinking wine. We had a beautiful meal and stayed up chatting well into the early hours. It was so lovely to have had such a girly outing and fantastic to spend time with Fionnuala. We have been friends since our first day at school, aged four years. We were both 42 years old now.

Fionnuala had lost her mum to motor neuron disease the previous year, so she completely understood grief and the loss of someone you adored. She was incredibly close to her mother. Her mother was amazing to me all my life. She always included me. She called me her adoptive daughter.

I loved going to Fionnuala's house as a child. There were three girls in her family, so that meant there were a lot of dolls. Dolls were sparse in my house, and any dolls that I did have were either decapitated or had shaved heads.

Filming day arrived. We arrived at the 'set' also known as Ranelagh Educate Together National School. Another 'coincidence', as I work at Midleton Educate Together National School. There was tremendous energy about the place. The sun was shining, and people were busying themselves. There were cameras and lights everywhere. To be honest, it took my breath away. I decided to embrace it all as I knew I'd never experience something like this again in my lifetime.

I travelled to the back of the school and entered through the opened door. I followed the corridor, smiling at people as I passed them. I stopped one lady and asked where I should go, she asked me my name, and when I told her that I was Katherine, she shouted: '*Katherine is here.*' At that moment, I realised that I was the star of the show, which made me both excited and nervous.

She ushered me to a small classroom labelled Junior Infants. I felt at home surrounded by all things school. She then introduced me to the director, marketing manager, lighting crew, creative director, makeup artist, animation team, and camera crew. It was amazing to be part of such a professional operation.

I was offered breakfast and then moved to the senior infant classroom, where the filming would occur. It felt like home as I had been teaching senior infants for the previous five years. I adore working with children. The shoot day took place in Dublin and was based in a classroom where you had to interact with the various characters, which would ultimately be brought to life through animation after the shoot day.

The team was fantastic; extremely professional, kind, warm, and friendly, out of this world. At lunchtime, I met the Head of Marketing at Vhi Healthcare, Adam Bacon. An absolute gentleman. We chatted over lunch.

The afternoon was busy, and we concluded the shoot around

four. The driver collected me and brought me to the recording studio. I had a sound check. I had to read back some of my own words. The words that would appear in the advert. Comments such as 'I'm a real hugger.'

The driver drove me to Dundrum shopping centre, where I reunited with Fionnuala. She had been meeting reps all day. We travelled home together.

A few weeks later, I received a copy of the finished ad. I was so uncomfortable seeing myself on TV, but I realised that I'm not used to seeing myself on TV because I am not an actor. That was my story, and there was nothing to fear.

I reminded myself that the reason that I did this was to highlight the importance of health. To emphasise that healthy, young people can get cancer and can get well again. I hoped that more than anything, it may help someone.

Health insurance was like a safety blanket to me throughout my illnesses. I had ten surgeries and procedures over ten years.

Whenever I have a lump or bump now, I know that I will be scanned straight away and access the best care. I know that Health is Wealth. Those were my father's words, words that I had put on his headstone at his grave. In my situation, it continues to be money well spent. Without it, I would not have had timely access to the healthcare I need.

I received the release date for the Vhi Healthcare testimonial advert. It would air on my birthday, August 7th. A heavenly message for me. I refer to heavenly messages as 'Joe-ism's' every time I feel a coincidence, I feel as though my dad is around. Thankfully I've had many 'Joe-ism's.' I explain to the children that when something that you want to happen, actually happens, that's a 'Joe-ism.' I don't believe in coincidence. Everything happens for a reason. What is for you won't pass you, and your path is mapped out.

Be gentle with yourself. Be kind to yourself. Speak to yourself with the same compassion that you show with loved ones. It is essential to change the words used in our defence or in reply to ensure that they are not aggressive so that the message can be heard. Your point of view matters because you matter. Practice a little self-love, read positive quotes and affirmations. Our most outstanding talent is much more potent than our biggest fear. Change your words and you will experience the magic of mindset change for you.

Thoughts provoked from reading this story

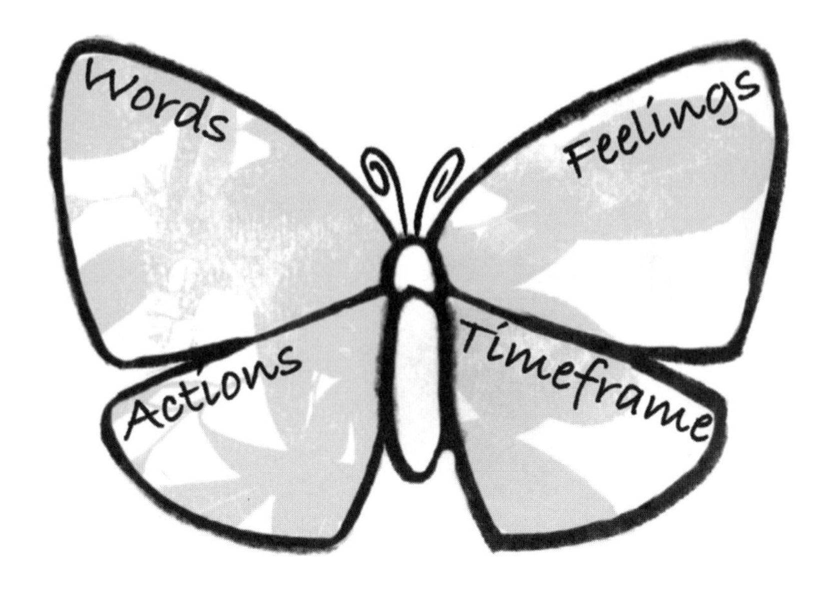

Notes:

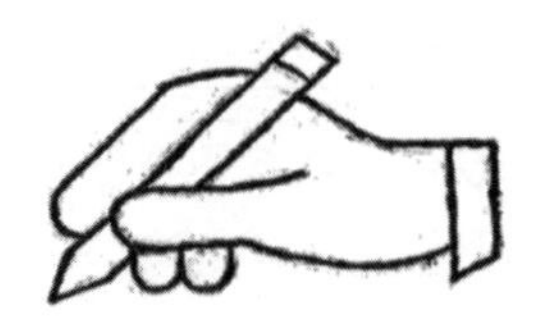

Story 5: Finding Your Voice

'Raise your words, not your voice. It's the rain that grows flowers, not the thunder.'

Rumi

Give your voice credit and value. What you think matters. How you feel, what you do, and what you say matters because you matter.

It is through standing up for yourself that you learn things about yourself. You begin to see clearly and learn about your strengths and weaknesses. You begin to grasp opportunities, understand your threats, and hope that you will cope with them.

I am reminded of a S.W.O.T. Analysis that I learned when working in Eircom a few years back. -Strengths, weaknesses, opportunities, and threats. It's a helpful strategy when dealing with a challenge. So what are the strengths, the weaknesses, the opportunities, and the threats?

My first memory of seeing someone find their voice was that of Princess Diana. I was stopped in my tracks as I watched her find and use her voice not just for her good but for the good of others. The first time that I saw her on the cover of a magazine, I was instantly taken by her femininity, inspired and moved by her vulnerability, passion, and deep love. I was utterly in awe of her style. She was beautiful.

She used her celebrity status to draw attention to unpopular and unpleasant causes. In June 1997, at Christie's in New York, 79 of her dresses were auctioned to raise 3.2 million for her favourite charities. The clothes were symbolic of the life she led, and they were being left behind. Two months later, the day that I graduated from college was the day of her funeral. I was graduating from college in Birmingham, so we were in the heart of the outpouring of people's grief for Diana. I remember the bouquets stacked up to my knees in the city centre. The atmosphere was sobering. There was no denying how important this lady was, not just to English people but to the whole world. It was unbelievable.

There are lots of inspirational people out there who are happy to share their learnings with us. For example, during the Covid 19 lockdown, I was fortunate to receive the recommendation to listen to an Instagram live by another inspiring lady, Niamh Connolly @ transformCBT. She spoke about our inner critic. She advised that we tune into ourselves and listen to what we say to ourselves. Listen to what we need. Similar to what I spoke about in my previous story about changing our voice and, in turn, changing our mindset.

Niamh's Instagram lives helped me cope with life in Covid and tackle some fears that I had buried deep in my head and heart. One, in particular, was, speaking up to people who hurt me. I find this particularly difficult, especially if they are the people whom I love. I become afraid that I will hurt them by telling them that they are hurting me. I feel that it is confrontational. I hate confrontation, and it brings me back to my childhood when my parents would fight and argue.

I have learned that we must not allow fears to hold us ransom to any kind of emotional abuse, neglect, or hurt. I learned that sometimes people are not aware that they are hurting us until *it is highlighted. If they love you, they will want to know if they are hurting you. Wouldn't you like to know if you were hurting someone you loved? I would hate to think that I hurt anyone, irrespective of whether I love them or not. Everybody deserves respect.*

Through the various checklists and questionnaires that Niamh shared I could pave a way through this challenge and find a way to speak up in a non-confrontational way by sticking to the facts.

So my question to you is. What do you want to say and do? You must have your say. It's time to stop internalising and to bring it externally so that you can heal and move on with your life. The most significant journey is the internal one, and the most remarkable bond is said to be that of father and daughter. Ours was an extraordinary one. Unique and unusual but an incredible journey that took us through divorce, cancer and grief. I had to lose my voice to find it.

Why is our inner voice so harsh and cruel to us? We deserve the best in life. We shouldn't stop ourselves or anybody else from grabbing life by the neck and living it. Sometimes you have to tell your inner voice to SHUT UP. Challenge yourself to speak up instead of swallowing toxic talk.

I am a huge fan of artist Charlie Mackesy. He became quite well known during the pandemic for his beautiful illustrations, which described the feelings and emotions of the world. One of my favourite lines was when he asked the question, 'What's the bravest thing you ever said? - Help'. Asking for help is a brave thing to do, there is no doubt.

If we could each find our voice and use it properly to reach our goals and fulfil our lives, I believe that the world would be a better place. I believe that we all have experiences to share. We all have a story to tell. So why not tell it? Why not share the highs and lows of the road that we have travelled and maybe help someone along the way or at the very least support someone to do something about a situation they might be struggling with?

Most of us love an old chin wag, a coffee, and a catch-up. We can help and support each other if we were only open to doing so with a lot more people.

I am not a big social media fan, I respect it for its ability to connect people. I also feel that people put up their best lives on these platforms. I can only imagine how that must make others feel if they see these images on a day when they think that their life is far from perfect. Why don't we aim for a balance and post pictures of our 'real' lives too? The car broken down, the mess from the dog when he attacked the rubbish bin or the child having a tantrum? Is there potential for a 'real book' where we can have a laugh about and vent about all the stresses and strains together in a supportive honest way and carry on?

We could just be on the same team if we could only be kind to each other and ourselves. Instead, we have an awful habit of looking at other men and women and then comparing ourselves to them. We ask ourselves frantic questions like - how does she/he do it? Why does she/he find it so easy? Why don't we give ourselves a break? Why don't we just celebrate the success of our fellow women/man and go easy on ourselves? You never know what's going on behind closed doors. A spotless house might be the coping strategy of someone trying to distract oneself from their broken heart. I know, that was me when I lost my dad to cancer. I had one of the cleanest houses in Ireland, not because I developed OCD or because I was super talented at juggling a busy life and still keeping a house on top form with ease. It was because I was losing control. I couldn't control my dad's fate but I could control my house. It was a difficult time. I was desperate, it was survival, and it was hard.

I often wonder, *why people's comments make us reflect inwardly so much? Why do they hurt? Why do we allow them? How can we put in a filter to help us sift out wasteful talk and purify it?* I've mentioned several times the analogy, to know all is to understand all. *Why don't people get to know all before they dump their judgment, or better still, why don't they help? Could we accept that there is a problem on their side, and as a result of their pain, they cause others pain?* It's like a kind of pay it forward but in pain instead of kindness. They are dispelling distress. It's essential to find a healthy way to do this.

As I've mentioned previously, my mother left home when I was a teenager. When I was in college in the UK, I travelled to and from Ireland to attend court for my parents' divorce. When I was pregnant with my second child, my dad was diagnosed with Non-Hodgkin's Lymphoma. When my son was three months old, while I was studying to sit the Leaving cert Irish paper, he contracted rubella resulting in night terrors. While studying for my teaching diploma, my dad went to St. James's for a bone marrow transplant. A month after getting permanency in my local school, I was diagnosed with thyroid cancer. The following year my dad received his second diagnosis. I had my gallbladder removed and was diagnosed coeliac. A year later I was diagnosed with bilateral sensorineural hearing loss and got hearing aids. I suffered numerous uterine conditions resulting in endometrial ablation, removal of polyps, fibroids, endometriosis and my fallopian tubes. Dad received his third diagnosis. Then he got diagnosed again, this time with two cancers. Furthermore, he was told to put his affairs in order. My bowel stopped working resulting in a bowel pacemaker drug. Twelve difficult months later, my Dad died. His death opened old wounds and created new ones.

I've noticed that I used the same coping skillset each time with each difficulty that I faced. I'm not saying that I have super survival ability or that I am even strong. What I am saying is that when faced with challenges, we can survive. We can keep going, one step at a time. As Winnie the Pooh said, '*you are braver than you believe, stronger than you seem, and smarter than you think.*'

The greatest lesson that I will move forward with is this. It's ok to stumble and to fall, we are all learning to survive, but I don't believe that it's ok to stay down. Get up and keep moving forward. When times get more complicated, every step you take, the bigger the victory, in my opinion. Surround yourself with positive people, if you can, they will hold your hand and help you. Always be respectful, significantly when others don't extend the same courtesy to you, communication is vital, and develop the skill of patience or, as my dad would call it, waiting in the long grass.

I stopped listening to advice and judgment unless those people are willing to help. I try to stay away from people who do not add value to my life. I have always found my voice through writing. When you write, you use the right side of your brain. The rational, responsible and decision-making part of the brain. Writing how you feel and what is upsetting or challenging you is equipping you to cope and find a solution. I believe that it is crucial to write about our feelings.

I always loved to write. When I was very young, I used to copy my dad's writing and his signature, and I would sit beside him in his office and doodle away to my heart was content. I was always fascinated with the art of writing. I loved poems, words, and song lyrics. I was amazed by the 'big words' used in the news at six o clock every evening, I would sit on the back of the couch behind my dad with my legs drooped over his shoulders, and I would listen to hear all the excellent words read in the news.

Before I was old enough to go to school, I would listen to the one o clock news with him. He came home for his dinner at one every day. That was a real country thing, to have your dinner in the middle of the day. I can still hear the music introduction of the news and Marian Finucan's voice. I had a little dark brown leather satchel bag with two buckles on the front, referred to as my school bag. I would carry that around with me just as my dad would bring his briefcase. His little mini-me. Dad loved to read the newspaper and did this every day. He loved the Irish Examiner or the Cork Examiner as it was called at the time, and read it cover to cover. Dad bought lots of business books and magazines. He inspired my love of reading and writing at a very young age.

I remember one time finding a large old brown suitcase in one of the top cupboards. Of course, we were not allowed into the top cupboards. But they were a great hiding place. I remember the night that I found that case, I was hiding on my brothers during a game of 'hide and seek' and I stumbled on the case and forgot about the game. It was full of dad's old school books. I remember thinking how old and unusual they looked. His writing was impeccable. There were many hard-back copybooks with dried flowers — papers in Latin and English, well-minded and preserved. When I questioned dad about them, he told me to leave them alone. Dad won a scholarship to College in the late sixties and studied agricultural science. As I write this, I realise that these books are still at home next door. I will ask my brother for them.

I loved finding rhyming words and writing my poems and I would write my version of the news and read it to my dolls and teddies. I had a big Styrofoam square that came with our new television. That was my TV. I drew buttons on the front and stuck two welding rods on the top for a TV aerial. I would sit for hours and write. I wasn't the brightest child, but I would consistently score high in the writing stakes.

Unfortunately, I was a very nervous child. I was a nail-biter and used to wet my pants a lot. This happened whenever I got nervous, like at Irish dancing class when I had to dance solos. I was a good dancer but didn't realise it at the time. I just thought that I was chosen so that I would focus my concentration. That's when I realised other benefits of dresses and skirts. It will run down your legs if you wet yourself in a dress or skirt, which was not as apparent as wet trousers.

I used to wet my bed a lot when I was a little girl. My brothers gave me the nickname, 'duck.' My mother put a plastic protective sheet on my mattress. As I write this, I wonder if my wetting incidents relate to my jaundice as a child. I remember my mother saying that I had weak kidneys, if there was such a thing. I hated myself for it, and it destroyed my confidence as a young girl. I remember stealing my youngest brother's plastic pants. Back in the day, plastic pants were put on over the terry towel nappies. I would take these plastic pants and wear them at bedtime, my oldest memory of problem-solving. I could therefore avoid another wet bed declaration in the morning and all the mocking that came with it. For as long as I can remember, I have had a health issue.

I was a bit of a loner as a child because I was quiet and shy. I didn't have many opportunities to mix with other children. I lived in the country and had four brothers. I had lots of company, and I loved to play with my brothers, but I didn't have other girls to relate to, and I was naturally very girly. I often wonder if that was because I wanted to differentiate myself from the boys. People who would call to dad's business would comment on the fine flock of boys he had. I don't blame them because I wore my oldest brother's hand-me-downs, *mainly featuring corduroy dungarees, polo necks, and brown pants. Sometimes, my neighbour used to make me dresses, and she also gave me her daughters hand me downs which I cherished.*

Writing became my friend. My escapism. A place where I could go and think about my thoughts, fears, and dreams. It was a safe place to express myself. I would sit beneath the cherry blossom tree in our garden and write about how I was feeling. I would analyse what I wrote and that helped me to cope and to problem solve. It also helped me to invent strategies to achieve my goals. It highlighted challenges that I needed to face. As soon as I wrote, I could see a plan. I would then write pros and cons lists and plan away until I was happy with where I was.

My oldest memory of using this strategy, stretches back to when my parents would fight, which was often. At the end of every day, I would arrive up to the sitting room with my notebook and fancy pencils. I would ask them both to list three things that they liked about each other, and then I would toddle off to bed happy. To be fair to them, they would nearly always play along. After all, they were good people. They just were not good together.

I wrote about my learnings as I faced different challenges, which helped me see personal growth and achievement. With each challenge that we face, we learn a new skill set. We can bring this unique skill set forward with us, almost armed for the future — a tough skin. There is strength in everyone if we look for it or have a reason to draw upon it. There is strength in finding strength. We can use that experience when dealing with future challenges.

I have a habit of doing a 'days analysis' whereby I write what was good and bad about the day and any constructive wisdom I have for myself. I discovered so much by using this strategy. It opened so many doors for me and closed toxic doors.

Sometimes I was unaware of what was affecting my mood, but when I started the 'days analysis' it was life-changing. I become aware. I was in tune with my head. It could be a person or an activity that was not good for my health and well-being. Once you highlight it to yourself, you can put a coping plan in place.

I recently had a problem: I was rushing to my son's school every day. I finish school at 2.20pm, and he finishes at 2.40pm. I wanted to collect him from school. It was one of the reasons why I changed careers to become a teacher. I could be in school when my children are in school and out of school with my children are on school holidays. Extreme juggling and hard work but worth it. However, I found it a constant battle to get to his school on time with traffic. I wanted to collect my son and get home to start the after-school routine, so I didn't have the time to hang around at his school chatting. To be honest, I also struggled to deal with some people who did not support me when my dad died. I just didn't have the strength to pretend to like them or even tolerate them. I knew that I needed distance from them until I could cope with my grief first.

By writing down my problem and all the feelings that went with it, I could develop a solution. My son was in the 5th class at the time. I permitted him to walk up to the corner shop, which involved no road crossing, and gave me an extra 10 mins to get to him, I didn't have to meet anyone, and he was thrilled to be trusted to walk, and he enjoyed the after school chats with his friends. He was self-regulated by the time he got into the car and was relieved of all school baggage. Baggage that he used to dump on me. This strategy helped me to turn a negative into a positive.

When Colin went into 6th class, his aunt, Carol, brought him home every day after school. He loved the responsibility that brought. Carol is a very caring person, and her act of kindness made life a little easier for me. There are good people out there who want to help. Communicate with them and ask them for the help that you need.

The following are three homemade strategies that I rely on to help me to cope. I call these 'three to be free' – to free my mind from hurtful talk.

1. Force thinking. Suppose someone makes a statement through a throwaway or smart comment. In that case, I tend to say 'sorry.' This allows them to repeat what they said and hopefully also to think about what they are saying.

2. Silence. Say nothing. I find that sometimes when I say nothing, it can spur people to ask, 'did you hear me?' So I reply, 'Yes, I heard you,' and say nothing else. Sometimes less said is best said. Leave the s**t with them. Don't pick it up.

3. Really! My final one helps with hurtful comments. I like to use the simple little word 'really'. For example, If someone says, 'Jesus, I haven't seen you in ages, I thought that you were dead.' Then I reply 'Really!' and nothing else. It's calling them up on their hurtful comment. Are you saying this to me? I always find it strange that it's not ok for you not to visit, phone, text, etc., but it's perfectly fine for them to do those things to you. Maybe you were struggling, being honest, it's all about them sometimes. People can be great, but you do need to teach some of them how to treat you. Command respect in a gentle, kind, and respectful way is my advice.

I try to turn negative situations into positive ones or find one positive from a negative situation — an exercise that took a lot of practice.

For example: When I got hearing aids, I used them as a positive lesson when working with children to show that physical disabilities don't hold you back in life. When I am trying to relate to children who are quietly spoken or shy. I play the '*It's not you, it's my hearing*' card. I look to the Vhi Healthcare testimonial advert to highlight the need for health insurance in this country. I am also grateful for reducing my medical bills as I don't qualify for a medical card or lifelong illness card.

When I studied for the leaving cert Irish exam & retraining as a teacher, while it was difficult it did offer a distraction from Colin's rubella, sleepless nights, and dad's cancer. It was a focus and a distraction — a positive step towards my future. When Mam left home, I learned a lot about coping with life's challenges. I learned to be independent and self-sufficient, that my children come first, and I must invest in my marriage.

When I faced a week of isolation for my radioactive iodine treatment, I set a challenge to get home faster than the one-week guideline.

I put my children into Play therapy following my cancer and the grief that dads death brought so that they can move forward happy, secure, and robust. I was acutely aware of the importance of this, having suffered trauma at home as a child.

While employed with Eircom in the corporate world, I used strategies that I learned at home as a teenager to help with managing my job. My love of writing, my love of analysis, my creative streak, my drive to fix a problem & to find a solution have helped me to deal with challenges.

My next battle would not be medical but instead an oral one. This took the shape of a fight with a company who assesses those of us who work and are on sick leave. I had never rung in sick to work.

The first time that I took sick leave was for my thyroid surgery for Cancer. Thankfully I never seem to get the small stuff like colds, flu and bugs, so I was always ready and able for work.

On a day in May, I got to speak with the staff of that organisation for the first time. I took the call and was asked by the lady how I was feeling. To which I replied that I was doing well and looking forward to getting back to normal. I explained my journey in full and answered each question. The lady issuing the questions was a qualified nurse. She said that I would have to speak with one of the doctors. Then, she invited me in for an interview. Yes, you read that right, an interview. This interview was set for 9am on the following Monday morning. I explained about my poor energy levels while I was building up my dose of Eltroxin medication. I was now on 150mg per day, but my blood was still not balanced. I was also suffering with, and was on antibiotics for, a severe kidney infection.

I arrived on time for my interview. I was asked a series of questions which I answered honestly. The female doctor asked me if I went out with friends for coffee while on sick leave. I answered no, my friends usually come to me. She asked me to explain my reasons for this. I told her that there were two reasons why I didn't feel comfortable going for coffee. Number 1, I lacked the confidence in my ability to maintain the required stamina. Number 2, I would feel it was wrong to have coffee dates while off work sick. She explained that going out with friends would help 'raise my mood' and return to work. I told her that there was nothing wrong with my mood. I never, thankfully, suffered from low mood until I lost my dad.

She went on to tell me that she thought that I was fit to return to work, in her opinion. I explained that I had received a return to work date in one week from my medical team. She said that I should return straight away. I was shocked.

I explained that I would never take advantage of my situation. I spoke about how hard I worked to become a teacher and how much I loved and treasured my job.

Then she delivered the most significant blow. She said, '*go back to work on Monday, and if you don't feel well, you could come back off work on Tuesday.*' I could not believe my ears. You would swear that I was on leave with the flu. I replied to her by summarising what she had asked me to do, to which she said, '*that's right, go back to work, and you can see how you get on. You can always sign out sick again.*'

I told her that the children would be upset if I came back after being off for 6 months and then go off again the following day. She told me that I held myself in high regard. I was again shocked. I explained that I was going on the recommendation of my medical team, and we were arguing over one week. I asked her to allow me the week to recover from my kidney infection as I was still building up my stamina. I felt that I was on trial. I honestly will never forget that lady.

The following day my school principal called me to say that a 'fit to work' recommendation was decided. He was as appalled as I was. I got onto my GP, who said that he would write to that organisation. They rejected his letter. They also rejected a letter from my school's management board recommending I complete my sick leave as per my medical team's recommendations. It felt wrong on every level. I could not accept this behaviour, leaving me with no choice but to report it and fight for justice, not just for me but all the other cancer patients who might have the unfortunate luck to meet with such a recommendation.

The agency that I went to was incredible, taking my case and achieving success. I was to return to work on the date that my *medical team saw safe for the school and me. I was so outraged but so pleased about what I had achieved. I firmly believe that if something is wrong and you do nothing about it, you become part of the wrongdoing.*

I also believe that if you can do something to pay it forward, you must do it. I do not regret it for one second. No one should have to go through that on top of what one is already going through. We all have a job to do, let us be kind and considerate while we do it. Find your voice and use it, not just for your good, but for the good of others too. What do you want to say or do?

Thoughts provoked from reading this story

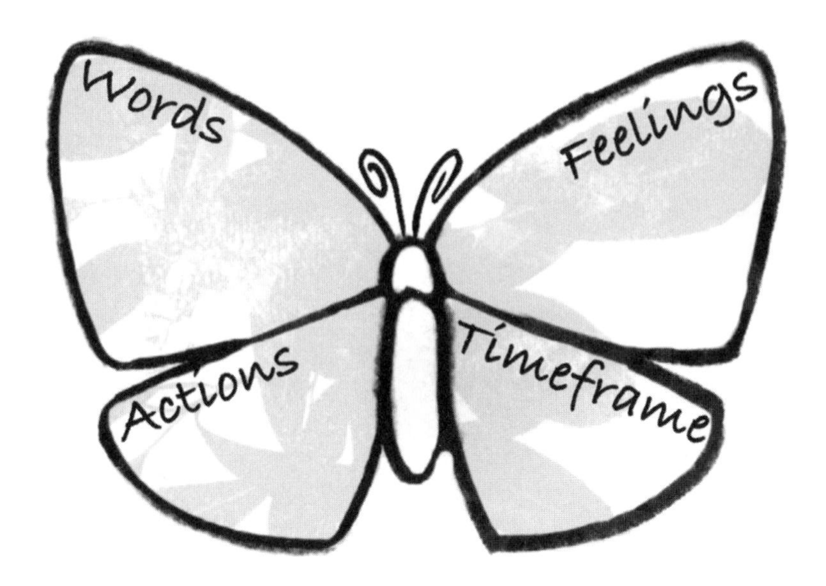

Notes:

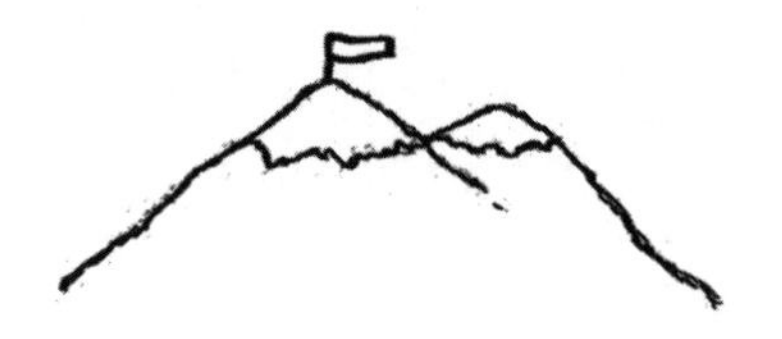

Story 6: Building Resilience

'The very things that hold you down
are going to lift you.'

Timothy Mouse, Dumbo

When life throws you a curveball, you can choose to either duck, get hit, or swing. The choice is yours. I believe that you can duck and avoid some things in life. Other times you get hit, and often you can and should fight back. Live your life.

There is an old saying that you become wiser with age. I am beginning to see evidence of that. As we move through life, we become wiser because we experience more and learn more as we navigate along. Through which we build resilience, we aim to enhance the quality of life by withstanding adversity and bouncing back from complex life events.

I am not, nor have I ever wanted to be tough. I just want to become strong enough to survive life's various challenges and safeguard myself against future challenges. I'd like to achieve this strength without hurting anyone in my path, even if they hurt me. No one is perfect, so the ability to say sorry is essential. You just never know what another person is going through. Be nice if you can. If you can't be nice, then be sorry when you can.

I try to remember that some people don't know us or get to

know us, and maybe they never will. Perhaps they have decided that they don't want to get to know us or our journey. Let them off. Their opinion no longer matters to you if you don't matter to them. We can all be guilty from time to time of judging a person before we know them. If you believe before you know, then that's your loss. My rule to myself is to treat people how I would like them to treat me. It might not be everyone's rule, but it's mine, and I'm sticking to it.

Communication is very important. Say that you are feeling vulnerable if you are feeling vulnerable.

'Vulnerability is not the opposite of resilience. Vulnerability builds resilience. Projecting perfection protects your ego but shuts people out and stunts your growth. Revealing struggles shows humility and humanity, opening the door to new sources of support and strength.'

@adamgrant on @mattzhaig's stories on Instagram

Recovering from a challenge takes perseverance, which is a continued effort. You learn new skills as you build resilience like flexibility or grit for example. Think about the action you took. Ask yourself was this the best thing to do for you. Should you have ducked and avoided the confrontation, or should you have got hit and suffered. Or should you have swung and fought back? Each situation in life is different, and each needs a different response. Life is a journey, a voyage of discovery. Each path that we choose to journey on builds our resilience for future trips.

It's been four years since I had *'that conversation'* with the oncologist. The conversation marked the beginning of the end of my world as I knew it and loved it. I've learned a lot since, primarily by accident and some through being in absolute survival mode. Love does conquer all, and I loved my dad. The tears flow as I write that. I always loved him, and I always will. He was an excellent teacher. I learned so much from him. I still draw on all the superb advice and try to live in the footsteps of positivity, determination, and strength that he walked in ahead of me. While he was firm, he would always acknowledge that you can't help how you feel. But you can help how you cope with your feelings.

When I was a little girl, I was a pure daddy's girl. My relationship with my dad was built on adoration and admiration. He would say, '*Kath, you're an awful Molly. Do you know that you're my pet?*' That's hard to write. I can still hear him say those words. It's still so raw, and it upsets and angers me that I cannot see him again. When my mother left home, my relationship with my dad changed to one of the 'boss.' It was a relationship built on trust and reliance. During the last nine years of his life, he referred to me endearingly as 'mother'.

It was a sunny morning in February 2008. I was six months pregnant with my son. Dad was employed by the Department of Agriculture, where he had worked for the past 35 years. We sat side by side in the waiting room of the Hospital with dad's best friend, Ger. We were waiting to meet with Professor Seamus O'Reilly. Little did we know at that point that Seamus would turn out to be someone who we would grow to understand and respect so profoundly in the nine years that followed. We chatted about the standard stuff as dad checked his watch. He didn't have time for these kinds of appointments, and they weren't leading to work for him. Dad loved his work. As well as being a district superintendent with the Department of Agriculture, he had his own business, *Dolphin Video Productions.* Dolphin is our *unusual surname and fitting for a man as unique as Joe Dolphin.*

The nurse appeared at the door and beckoned to us to follow her to room 2. We entered and sat like three bears in a row as dad did the introductions. He referred to me as 'my young one'. Seamus was a warm person. I could tell that from the get-go. There was a lovely relaxed vibe in the room as Dad pointed out that Seamus was also a Galway man. So all was perfect until it wasn't.

*Seamus said those words, '**Joe, your results are back, and you have Non-Hodgkin's Lymphoma!**' I could feel the weight of my bump and my heart. That day I will forever remember as the beginning of the end. I will never forget the delivery of his diagnosis. That was the first time that I had experienced heartbreak. I heard and felt my heart break.*

Dad was my rock. We were the dream team. I would not decide on anything without his approval and if I upset him, it was the end of the world for me. But, we had it all worked out and it worked well. This threat to his life and our foundation was incredible. But something kicked in. Love kicked in and we decided to push forward with whatever Dad had to do medically to get better.

To say that he was a brilliant patient would be an understatement. He was remarkable. He spat in the face of cancer, then he danced upon it. He left every appointment with the plan to head off dancing. He had the most beautiful pair of black leather dancing shoes. He was the most beautiful dancer. He had the grace and presence that commanded a room and captivated the dance floor. As soon as you spent time with my dad, you were devoted to him. The most charismatic soul I know. The stamina with which my dad powered through each stage was inspirational. The funny and yet extraordinary memories he has left me with will help me continue growing and healing.

One of my favourite funny memories of his cancer journey occurred during his first diagnosis. I decided that I would shave his head so that he wouldn't experience hair falling out every day. He went along with it. However, after a week, his hair started to grow back again. I shaved it again. It grew back again. At his three monthly check-in appointment with his oncologist, he asked when his hair would fall out because he was sick of shaving it. It was explained to him that he would not lose his hair on that particular drug potion. I thought that dad would kill me. He never shaved his head after that, even in the years that followed when treatment caused him to lose his hair. Instead, he embraced little tufts of hair that jutted out of his nearly bald head.

Life's challenges saw our relationship evolve and change over the years through positivity and love, to blossom into one of pure self-discovery. It's incredible that while you put someone you love first all your life, you can become so fulfilled. You can learn so much about yourself and the world around you when you try to do the right thing each time. I was blessed to have been my daddy's girl. It gave me incredible love, a unique bond, a connection where two became one on a remarkable journey of hope, compassion, respect, and spirit. My journey with my dad brought me great joy. I owe him so much, more than he will ever know. It puts a smile on my face every time I think of him and all we've been through together.

He was hilariously nerdy and hugely popular. He had a way of keeping you grounded at all times with few words of wisdom, though, sometimes smartly delivered and hard to hear. He had the most amazing hugging arms, which I can still feel today if I close my eyes. In the days after his death, I wrapped myself in his favourite red jumper so that I could feel his warmth. It takes time to process it all. We can all learn something from each other. We are all strong, and we only know of our strengths when we face challenges. I do believe that each challenge makes us stronger and more appreciative of what we have. Be kind to yourself and just do the next right thing and you will get there.

Always show respect to others but respect yourself too by minding yourself through coping strategies. Other people's opinions of you are none of your business. Leave it with them. Your life is not a court trial. I have many rules that I have put in place for myself following a lot of pain suffered. My main rule is to stop listening to advice and judgment unless those giving it are willing to help. Another rule is to surround myself with positive people.

I am going to share three more strategies that I found helpful along the way. I called these - *Three to see* – three strategies that have helped me see the light at the end of the tunnel.

1. Laughter

The most significant one being laughter. That might sound ridiculous, but it does work. I wouldn't be here if it weren't for the humour. I have found laughter to be not only a tonic but a lifeline. Finding opportunities to laugh is essential. Even on my darkest day, Dad's funeral, I laughed at some stories about him. He always makes me smile. He makes me sad too. I tear up when I mention or hear his name. I now understand that with love as deep as ours, I will never be the same without him. The loss is too significant. But I can be the best version of myself. I can now live each day with his loss beside me and not on top of me like it was. Finding laughter, being kind to myself, and crying have all helped me to move forward. Laughter is everywhere. We all know where to find laughter. I have a fantastic group of girlfriends who provide me with buckets of laughter.

2. Communicating

Talking helps too. It is in the knowing that you are not alone. Surround yourself with joyful people. They are out there and when you find them, never let them go. Something as simple as picking up the phone and asking for 'help' can be a game-changer. Inviting a friend for a coffee can help, a trip to the shops, a good book, a YouTube clip, a song, a walk, or a run. There are lots of things that we can do together. Together is key. We are not alone. Don't be alone if you don't want to be.

3. Be honest

Be honest (not hurtful). Be you. Be authentic. You being authentic means coming from a genuine place within. It is when our actions and words are congruent with our beliefs and values. It is being ourselves, not an imitation of what we think we should be or have been told we should be. Some factors influence and hinder authenticity - Anxiety and worry are just two. Worry is a prayer for the things that you don't want to happen. Don't worry. My counsellor told me that high anxiety is when you overestimate the danger and underestimate your coping ability. Never underestimate your ability to cope.

I know that my most powerful thought in the aftermath of my mother leaving home was my deep desire to build a good life for my future family and me. So I got on a plane at 18 to attend college in the UK. We found a way to make it work. I came home as often as I could. It was selfish, considering that my dad and the boys needed me at home. But they all supported me and getting an education and career were essential things to my father. He wanted the best for his children. He showed us that when the going gets tough, the tough get going. He put us first.

While in college, I worked every summer with Irish distillers at the Jameson Heritage Centre in Midleton, near my home, and this helped me support myself while at college. I knew that I would have to work part-time in the UK. So I decided that if I had to work, work would have to work for me. There were plenty of work opportunities at the college. There were three restaurants on-site because the college was popular for its catering courses. Jobs in the restaurants were like gold because you got to eat good food cheaply. I also worked in the library and resource centre, which was great because I had first dibs at the good books. I believe that if you want to do something, try to find ways to make that work for you. You can do anything. It takes a little innovative thinking and a bit of perseverance, and you will find that you build remarkable resilience along the way, which will help you with the next obstacle.

Some points to note:

> My dad often said, '*you can't help how you feel.*' Your feelings are not a choice, but your actions and behaviours are a choice.
>
> Ask yourself if you can focus on what matters to you and control your thoughts and actions.
>
> When you point your finger at someone, remember, three fingers are pointing back at you. You have the power to make a change.
>
> Fear builds walls, and love builds bridges.

'We can do no great things,
only small things with great love.'

Mother Theresa

The Big 'C' came back, you see!

A couple of months into my teaching career, my dad was diagnosed with Non-Hodgkin's for a second time. It was 2011. He had a three-year break, and now it's back. I remember selfishly thinking that whatever about getting cancer once, twice was just not fair. However, dad tackled this diagnosis just as he did the first with great determination and positivity. Following his treatment, his medical team recommended having a bone marrow transplant in Dublin that December. While the transfer was successful, the recovery was cruel. Dad ended up in ICU with a fragile heart. I refer to this time in my life as the 'treadmill period.' It looked like this. I would come from school, sort the kids, drive to Dublin to see dad, come home, do some work for my teaching as I was in my Dip year, and try to catch 4-5 hours of sleep. Then do it all again the next day.

Christmas 2011 was the first Christmas that we were not at home together, and it was pure torture. On the 6th January 2012, which is also referred to as 'women's little Christmas', I took dad home from St James Hospital in Dublin. He saw that as one of his most significant achievements, and it was. He was incredible. He was fragile and he had a long journey to recovery ahead. He dropped from 16 stone 2 pounds to 10 stone 4 pounds. He had lost his big hugging body but gained a third chance at life, which he grabbed with both arms.

Dad spent most of 2012 building himself up, and it was non-stop for him. He had to build up his body weight, muscle tone, energy, and immune system. I went up home to him every morning for an hour before I went to school to do as much as I could to set him up for the day ahead. Every day after school myself and the children went home to him and stayed there until the children's bedtime. It was lovely to have them there with dad. They got to know and appreciate him which was lovely to experience. Maur went up to dad every night until his bedtime. It was busy and it involved a lot of juggling but it was fantastic to be able to do it for him. In October, he got pleurisy, a setback, but he got up from it all and got stronger again.

We got through it together, one day at a time. He was getting back to his usual self of working and dancing. He looked at life as if the world was ending tomorrow. Dad loved his life, and as I said before, there weren't enough hours in the day for him. Despite his time in hospital being a battle for us, we did laugh a lot too. Laughter was something that came easy to all of us, and we were a very witty bunch, if I do say so myself.

I remember the nurses coming in to take Dad's blood pressure. Dad would have all his technology plugged into every available socket. I use to refer to it as his hospital office. The nurse would kindly ask '*Joe, which plug can I take out to plug in the Blood Pressure machine?*' to which dad would reply '*none*'. I remember how he would time the different drips in the chemo ward, and he had worked out that if he called the nurse when there were four minutes left in each bag by the time she would come and check him, she would be right on time with no time lost. By lunchtime, his treatment would be completed. He didn't have to stay for lunch as that would have been a waste of an hour of his life. He didn't have time for treatment. When he received the dates for treatment, he would always ask to reschedule if it clashed with his work. He was too busy living to be sick. I recall the nurses telling him to go home and rest after his treatment, and he would laugh and say, '*I'm off dancing for the night. I have my good shoes in the car*'. Cancer was just something that he had to go through. His treatments were just another thing that he had to do.

When dad finished his bone marrow transplant in 2012, part of his ongoing treatment plan was an immune booster treatment every three weeks. He got a port put into his chest. That was where his drugs would be administered. He never complained. He was so grateful that there was a plan. He showed incredible resilience.

Brian!

Brian Hurley was like a brother to me and my brothers. He grew up about a mile from our home but practically lived at our house. He was always the one that thought up of the next fun thing to do. We have so many happy memories and stories about Brian. He was the first person, outside of my brother's to call me 'Ka'. I always felt that there was something special about him and I was very fond of him. He was supportive and loyal and we all loved him.

He had absolutely no fear, I remember when we were teenagers, I called Brian up one night because there was a guy hanging around outside and we were afraid. Brian didn't bat an eyelid, he arrived up minutes later dressed in camouflage clothes and frightened the life out of the man.

He was very supportive through the years. I remember when I was trying to breastfeed Mia and failing miserably at it. Brian called up to visit, he could see that I was upset and he asked me what was wrong. I explained about the challenges that I was experiencing with breast feeding. Brian had the ability to be strong and sensible when you needed him to be. He understood what it was like to be a parent and he was a fantastic dad to his two girls. I looked forward to their visit every Sunday morning. He advised me to do what was right for me and he left. Ten minutes later he returned to my door with a box of Aptamil formula and told me to make bottles. I couldn't believe it. I will always remember his support. He was such a softie and I loved him for that.

Some of his hospital appointments over lapped with dads so their room was turned into a community centre and we had many a happy night hanging out with the two of them in what should typically have been more sobering visits. He always made the darkness bright.

He knew how to live and he taught us all a thing or two about making the most out of life. It was ironic because he squeezed so much into what was to be a short life. Brian battled cancer for a short 12 months and lost this battle in April 2012, aged 38 years. He was a husband, a dad of two beautiful girls, a son, a brother, a friend and he was like a brother to us. Rest in peace Brian. I never thought when writing and delivering Brian's eulogy that the following year I would be delivering baby Séan's, then writing and delivering dads a few short years later. Words can be so very powerful.

Baby Séan

Ruth and I have been friends for years. Our firstborn children were born six weeks apart. Shane is Maur's longest friendship. I have known Shane all my life as he grew up with my brothers. I always felt that Shane and Ruth would be a good match so I pushed them together on a night out and it was a match, a match made in heaven if I do say so myself.

On the day that Brian died, the lads had gone to be with Brian while the girls gathered at my house. That was the day that Ruth told me that she was expecting Baby Séan. I was absolutely delighted for her and Shane and felt a particular connection to Séan instantly. It was surreal to be losing one beautiful person while expecting another. Life is so very strange sometimes.

I had my biopsy the day Séan was born. On February 1st 2014, aged 16 months, Séan went to the angels. February 1st is St Blaise's day and blessing of the throats; I was diagnosed with thyroid cancer of the throat.

On Feb 4th I stood at his graveside and released 16 balloons, one for each month of his life. Three short years later to the day, my dad would join Séan and Brian in heaven. The day after Séan's funeral I had my thyroid uptake scan and went into remission. Sometimes there are no words.

Me! You're kidding!

I began to think that things might just settle down, or so I hoped. However, peace was not to come just yet.

In October 2012, I found a lump in my throat. I had noticed a change in my voice. The children at school noticed it too, but I thought it was because I had recently been under a lot of stress. Dad was unwell, and me having to juggle teacher training, home, family, friendships, work, and life.

I decided to get it checked out. So dad brought me to an appointment with a gifted head and neck surgeon, an otolaryngologist. It was unusual for dad to be on the other side of the appointment. In *many ways, it's easier to be the patient than the carer, in my opinion. You willingly take on the pain yourself once the ones you love are spared from suffering.*

The doctor did a physical examination of my neck. He then did an internal look at the nose and throat using a tiny camera on a tube that goes up your nose and down your throat. It's not painful, but it is uncomfortable—a bit like a covid test.

He said that everything looked fine. He said that he would like to book me for an ultrasound to look at the nodule/lump on the right side of my neck. He said that he wasn't worried. The ultrasound was booked for two weeks later.

The radiographer scanned my neck with great detail. Then she left the room and returned with a senior radiographer, who then checked my neck. The first radiographer then said that she would now perform a fine needle aspiration in my neck. That was sore. The senior radiographer informed me that he would be doing a second fine needle aspiration. To be honest, I thought that he meant on the same side because the first one didn't work. But, he turned my head to my right and took a fine needle aspiration from the left side. I was puzzled because I only had a lump on my right side, or so I thought. I got a funny feeling in my gut but said nothing. Finally, the radiographers told me that my ultrasound results would be sent to the consultant.

When I got out to my car, I began to wonder how I would turn my head in traffic. I thought that I was only having a neck ultrasound. I didn't know that I would end up with two fine needle aspirations. To be honest, they did hurt a bit, and they were sore each time that I had to turn my head to look left and right. I drove home and went straight to visit dad. It was midday at this stage. Dad asked why I wasn't in school. I told him that I had a training course.

Yes, I know I lied. But, I always figured that white lies were ok if they were selfless and protected someone else. I had put a scarf around my neck because my dad was as cute as a fox, and I knew that he would spot something.

Dad had been unwell for the week. He had what presented as a severe dose of the flu. I had pleaded with him to go to the doctor, but I had no success. Finally, that day he agreed that he would call the doctor. The doctor decided to come to see him at home. Dad was adamant that he was not going to the hospital and had convinced the doctor to give him another antibiotic and see how things looked in 24 hours. While outside the house, I told the doctor that I was very concerned about dad. He agreed that dad was very unwell and said he would speak with Dad's oncologist and revert.

A couple of hours went by and dad called me to tell me that his oncologist wanted to admit him to the hospital, and he asked if I could bring him. This was no problem typically, but today I had a dodgy neck. So I called Ger and asked her to come with us so that she would walk dad into the hospital and she could be my eyes on the road too. It all worked out.

That night I went back up to the hospital to see dad, and he had been diagnosed with pleurisy. He would spend two weeks in hospital. The first thing he said to me when I entered his room was, '*What's going on with your neck?*' I had no choice but to tell him.

When dad got out of the hospital, I had my follow-up appointment with my otolaryngologist. Maurice and I had decided to make his All-Ireland Master Angler competition trip into a small getaway for ourselves. We hadn't had a break on our own in years. So the plan was to stop off at my appointment and head to Donegal straight after.

The doctor was happy with my fine needle aspirations

because no cancer was detected. This was great news. However, he did say that I had two tumours in my neck — one on either side. One was 4 cm and the other 2cm. He advised that I have the 4cm one removed and the right side of my thyroid, and then down the road, if the other tumour grew, that could be removed. So, to be honest, I asked him why he doesn't remove both together. The thoughts of having my throat slit twice didn't sit well with me. Neither did the idea of waiting for the other tumour to grow. He explained that if he removed both tumours, he would also have to take my thyroid gland because the tumours were embedded in it. I would then have to go on a thyroid replacement drug for life. It was a lot to think about.

I left the appointment and went to meet Maur back at the car. I told him what I had just been told. He asked if I wanted to go home. I replied that I didn't. I needed the break. We needed the break. So we carried on. To be honest, it wasn't the best decision that I ever made because Maur was gone off fishing all day while I had too much time on my hands. It's ironic how I had craved free time for years and then when I get it I needed the opposite. I need to be busy distracting my head.

Two weeks later, I was admitted to hospital for my partial thyroidectomy. I met with the surgeon before my operation. I asked him again if I could have a complete thyroidectomy. He told me that a partial was all I needed for now. I told him that I understood that, but I would prefer to have it sorted now and move on. He agreed to do a total thyroidectomy and removal of the two tumours.

My surgery took three hours. Post-surgery went fine. My calcium levels dropped temporarily, which is expected as the parathyroids make the calcium, and they are next-door neighbours to the thyroid. Two days post-surgery, I was discharged. I went home to recover. A week post-operation, I developed the worst throat infection ever. I will never forget the pain as long as I'm alive. My throat was on fire. It was burning. I thought that I would lose my mind with the pain. I had a course of antibiotics and steroids, and I turned a corner. I started on the drug Eltroxin, my new lifelong buddy. I started on 50mg and built up from there. It takes a while to work out what dosage your body needs. My body required 200mg per day.

It was just over two weeks since my thyroidectomy, and I was due back to work on Monday. However, I first had to attend the outpatient department to get the results of my histology report and have my thyroidectomy scar checked. I asked my friend Finn if she would like to come to Cork for a look around. It was two weeks to Christmas. Any excuse for a trip to the shops. The only thing that I had to get was a fairy / angel-like costume for Mia for her second class Christmas play at school.

I told Finn that I would be in and out of my appointment within a few minutes, or so I thought, and then we could meet our other friend Marguerite for lunch and hit the shops. I went into the outpatient waiting room, and when my name was called, I went into the doctor's room which was also my dad's doctor's room. It turns out that my doctor worked under dad's doctor, I got a strange sense of Déjà Vu.

I sat in the chair, and he began to speak. He asked me how I was feeling. I explained that I was after a vicious week, I was now feeling great. He checked my scar. All was good. Then he told me that the operation was successful.

However, the histology report came back, and it showed that I had cancer. Papillary Thyroid Cancer, to be exact. I reminded him that my fine needle aspirations showed that my tumours were benign. He explained that the needle could only pick up a sample in the area it enters with FNA. It can't test the whole tumour. Histology is very sensitive and misses nothing. It didn't.

The rest is a bit of a blur. However, I remember the doctor speaking very positively. He commented that I was lucky that I chose a total thyroidectomy and that it was behind me, and to be honest, he was right. My tumours and thyroid had been removed before I knew that I had cancer and needed them gone. So I was well on my way.

A lovely nurse appeared. I could not hear her name or remember her face. I just remember her presence being warm and friendly. She brought me to another room and asked questions about my health, family history, and work. Then, she told me about the radioactive iodine treatment, which was chemotherapy for Thyroid cancer. It involved taking a powerful radioactive iodine tablet in the nuclear medicine department and then entering an isolation room for one week until the radiation was reduced to a safe level. This treatment would remove all the remaining thyroid tissue.

The nurse said that I would stay on my Eltroxin for a couple of months and build up my strength. Then the plan would be to do the treatment in March. I left the outpatient department with my information leaflets, appointment card, busy head, and a heavy heart. I didn't have much time to process it. I had to think of others. How would I tell them? How would I cope with yet another challenge? I stood with my back to the wall of the hospital to gather myself. I wasn't afraid, I think that I was just lost. I knew that I should phone Maur first and then my dad before I went back to the car to Finn. She was happy about doing work stuff and had told me not to rush.

I phoned Maur, and I decided that I would do the happy version of the news, so I told him that I was diagnosed with Thyroid cancer, but I was already half sorted because I had the surgery already. He was quiet, but he acted contently. He is very logical, and he is also solid and selfless. He would never add to my pain with his concerns. Weeks later, he told me that his heart stopped beating for a second. He got a fright.

I called dad and took a slightly different approach with him. I told him that I'd joined the 'C' club. He was a seasoned cancer patient at this stage, having had his two experiences in 2008 and 2011 and a bone marrow transplant. He was calm and controlled. However, he did call me an hour later to inform me that he had done his research, and he was happy that I was both in good hands and well on my way to recovery. But, unfortunately, he liked to worry behind closed doors. When dad died a very close friend of his told me that he only ever remembers seeing my dad being rattled once, that was when I was diagnosed with cancer.

I went back to Finn, and I didn't say anything. I just showed her the leaflets with 'Thyroid Cancer' on them. She replied, '*Jesus girl do you want to go home?*' I told her that I didn't. I wanted to meet Marguerite, and get Mia's dress.

We drove into the city and went to the restaurant. I couldn't eat. I had lost my appetite. I told them to eat without me, and I stepped outside to get some air. Minutes later, Finn followed me and said to me that she thought that we should go home. I asked her if I could get Mia's dress, she said, of course.

We headed off to Marks and Spencer's. I got her a beautiful blue Cinderella dress. Blue was her favourite colour at the time. As soon as I had paid for the dress, I felt weak in myself. Fionnuala suggested getting a hot chocolate because she thought I could do it with a sugar rush. She was right. It was exactly what I needed. I then told her that I wanted to call my family. She was a fantastic support to me that day. Thank God I didn't go to the appointment alone. Even though I was not afraid, I was not myself. As soon as we had inhaled the hot chocolate, we went home. I decided to focus on

Christmas.

Straight after Christmas, I got a call from the hospital to tell me that they had decided to bring my radioactive iodine treatment forward. The radioactive iodine would absorb any thyroid tissue that wasn't removed during the surgery. This meant that I would have to come off my drug, Eltroxin, ultimately as there had to be no trace of it in my body for the treatment to work. I refer to this as the great come down. It's like the worst hangover. But the radioactive iodine needed to be absorbed.

The week before I went into isolation was spent getting the kids and the house organised. Mums tend to think that the world will fall in if we are gone for a week. I was setting a target to be out in three to four days. Targets are always good to distract oneself and are a great diversion from the stress at hand.

I felt invigorated by the challenge ahead while I felt sad and worried for my kids, Maurice and Dad. Although Dad being Dad, reminded me that I was to stay well enough away from him with my radioactive waves because he didn't want to be sick again. He always made me smile and focus.

The dangers of radiotherapy and radioactive iodine might speed up cancer that might already be in your body asleep. It was also obviously dangerous to be around pregnant women and children. Cork ARC was exceptional in preparing me for the isolation unit and giving me great words to explain it to the kids.

D day arrived, Monday 3rd February 2013. Maurice brought me to the hospital. I was greeted by the nuclear medicine guy, who went through the paperwork. First, my blood was checked to see if I was utterly underactive in terms of thyroid functioning. I couldn't control my bowel, I had a swollen head, and the vision in my right eye was coming and going, and I have never experienced tiredness like it.

I said my goodbyes to Maur and headed off to the isolation unit. It was just off the ground floor of the CUH. I had so much stuff with me. There was a simple rule. Anything that you bring in, you can't bring out. So this was an excellent opportunity to get rid of clothes that I no longer wanted, including my husband's old work t-shirts. His shirts didn't work out, though, because when my body heated up, I would smell engine oil, so it's just as well no one was allowed near me! I knew that I would be having three showers a day because it would help remove the radioactive iodine from your body quicker. So that meant lots of clothes and towels. Everything would be taken away and burned after me.

The only thing that I struggled with was my phone. That was my only connection to the outside world. I am a bit of a baby. I don't like to be on my own for too long. The doctor agreed to wrap my phone in cling film. If the phone worked through the clingfilm, then I could take it in. It worked, and I was relieved. Friendly people will always stick out in your mind. He was an angel.

I knew that other than the clothes on my back, my phone would be the only thing that I would walk out within my possession. So there was a sense of freedom rather than fear from that, to be honest.

The nuclear medicine guy, dressed in what I can only describe as a spacesuit, administered the radioactive iodine tablet. Then he promptly left the room, where I quickly became highly radioactive. I refer to it as the 'prisoner feeling.' It was a case of mind over matter, to be honest, like other mums, I used to go to the toilet for a bit of peace. At this point in my life, I swore that I would never look for an escape from them again. But, of course, this didn't last as I am human. Every mum needs headspace, even if it is only an escape to the loo.

I began to scan the room and take in my new surroundings. There was a small kitchen area at the end of the room. A lovely lady who had received the treatment before me donated the kitchen. How beautiful was she? Bless her. There was a TV, a bed and an ensuite. Everything was covered in cling film, every switch, the tv remote, the handles and the phone. There was a landline in the room, and this was how the medical team could speak with you and call with any questions.

I spotted a hatch in the wall. I asked him what it was. He explained that that was the hatch that they would pass my food through. It was also the hatch that they would access to test my radioactive iodine levels daily. There was a corridor between this hatch and the actual hospital so you were separated from the outside world.

I settled in, had a good look around. I opened every cupboard and the fridge. There were yogurts, cheese, milk, and fruit in the refrigerator. To which I added my chocolate stash. My sister-in-law, Breda, made me some lasagne and shepherd's pie for my stay. I love my food, and she is a fantastic chef. There was a kettle and tea and coffee on the counter.

I got changed for bed and turned on the tv. I settled down for the evening. I was so delighted to have my mobile. I phoned home, and that was great. The hospital told me that I could give the extension number for my room to my husband. I was thrilled. Maur bought Mia a landline for her bedroom, we felt that she was too young for a mobile phone. She was able to call me in my room. That telephone line was a lifeline for us.

The following morning I heard a knock at the hatch. Somebody spoke and said, '*Katherine can you stand behind the line on the ground while we pass you in your breakfast.'* There was a line about three feet back from the hatch, which was a marker as to how close to the hatch I was allowed to be for the safety of the hospital staff. I took in my breakfast and settled into my first full day there. There was a vast Ballygowan water cooler in the corner of the room. I was told to drink a lot of water. Three litres a day because it would help to dispel the radioactive iodine from my body, there were several refill bottles also.

The hatch was opened a total of four times a day for seconds at a time. For breakfast, lunch, dinner, and a radioactive iodine wave check. I never passed anything out. It was all binned. There were four bins along the wall, each labelled, one for general rubbish like packaging, one for clothes and towels, one for sanitary disposal, and one for food waste.

Later that day, I started to get a tightness in my throat, which just got worse by the minute. I did get a fright, but the fantastic staff were on the other end of the phone. I called the nurse. She contacted the doctor. He called me on the phone, and he reassured me that it was all normal. The radioactive iodine treatment was doing what it was supposed to do, kill off remaining cancer and the thyroid cells. He prescribed steroids, and by the end of that day, I was managing away fine. Little did I know that four years to the day, I would lose my dad to cancer.

On day two, he returned to check my radioactive measurements. This was done by sticking what I can only describe as a traffic speed gun into the door hatch while I stood on the line on the ground. This procedure would continue daily.

The nuclear medicine guy was very impressed by the speed the iodine was leaving my body. This was great. My plan to get out early was working. The days passed, my radioactive levels had dropped considerably, and he told me that I could go home. I was thrilled. I left that room in such a powerful mood. What an accomplishment. I didn't go off my head. My own company was actually alright. Now the home plan starts.

That was the most unusual return home ever. Generally, if I have been in hospital, I return home to hugs and kisses and a good old catch-up with the kids. But, this time was so very different. I was discharged with a yellow skull and crossbones warning card to alert people to my recent radioactive iodine treatment. I was still quite radioactive but safe at a distance of three feet back.

I couldn't sleep in my bed, instead, I was in the spare room which my husband had to lock me into each night. At night your body temperature can rise, which could be very dangerous for those around me. I was afraid that the children would come into me at night, so I opted for the locked door for their safety. Of course, the prison feeling was still there, but at least I was at home.

I couldn't touch anything. I had my own hand towel. I often look back and laugh at that time because it was challenging to make sense of the three feet rule. Some days I'm sure our dog was radioactive as she used to brush against me. Contact of any sort was strictly forbidden. This was a massive struggle for the kids and me. I am a very tactile person, and I would refer to myself as 'a real hugger' as I said in the Vhi Healthcare testimonial advert. I was home, they could see me, but they can't touch me even when they cry. It was challenging to explain this to young children. I used to tell them that dangerous invisible rays were coming off me that they couldn't see. They were magic. They just had to believe this. Thank God my kids had great imaginations.

Those six weeks made me call on every morsel of strength that I had in me. Confined to a chair during the day and a locked room at night, I could not hug my children, help with their homework or cook a meal. I couldn't lift my arms above my head, so Maurice had to dress me. I have not been dealt the best health card, but he was a gift that I cherished.

I was not allowed to hug or kiss or even sit close to anyone. I had to stay a meter back from everyone. I couldn't share a bed with my husband. I couldn't share a towel. To be honest, I couldn't touch anything in the house because that could cause a risk to them. I slept in the spare room. I had to be locked in at night because my son would sleepwalk, and I was afraid that he would get too close to me while I slept. This went on for 6 weeks. They were long weeks. Long days. But they passed, and with every day, I got stronger.

At the end of the six-week contact ban, I was delighted and thankful to be able to hold my kids and husband again. Dad had built up a bit of fat, and he was well on the way to rebuilding his famous hugging arms. So all was good, and life was getting back to normal.

Mia's communion was coming up, and I was in the process of making her dress when I got sick, so I had to abandon that plan. I used to be very headstrong about my ideas, and I would have found it very difficult to give up on any dream. But making Mia's dress was a non-runner. With my priorities in check, I boarded the train to Kildare, where one of my most special friends Helena, would be waiting to collect me to bring me to her house in Wicklow.

Helena's home is a second home to us, and we try to go up there as often as possible. Helena and I were housemates while in college in Birmingham in the late nineties. So we have been solid friends for over 25 years. Helena had booked us into a communion dress shop to help source a dress for Mia. We got a beautiful dress. We were all happy.

The next day we headed back to Cork on the train. I usually hate being the centre of attention, and I hate to ask for help in general. However, if I could have worn a badge on my coat or a sticker on my head that said *'cancer survivor'* or *'just after treatment a couple of months ago'*, I would have. The train was crowded, and I was weak as a kitten standing holding onto two kids, a communion dress, and our bags. That was the longest journey I was ever on in my life. But we did it together.

I will never part with that dress. However, the original dress that I was making with the support of a local lady was eventually completed, and I donated to a local girl for her big day the following year in May, the same month that I went into remission.

Every month following my blood work, I increased my Eltroxin dose until I was steady on 200mg a day. My endocrinologist decided that my drug dose should be suppressed to protect me from reoccurring Thyroid cancer. That was difficult because I knew that meant that I would never have the same energy levels again. I am like the bunny in the Duracell advert. I like to be going non-stop. However, this was my new life, and I had to embrace it.

I was assigned an endocrinologist. My cancer was endocrine so that means that an endocrinologist will monitor me for the rest of my life. I have now moved to annual appointments. I am disappointed that I will never be free from tests, scans, and consultants, but there is security in that too. I am minded and will be forever.

My cancer has affected my life in so many ways. I don't qualify for a medical card, so I must pay for all my medical expenses. I have a life long illness. I am coeliac, and the cost of that diet is my battle. I have bilateral sensorineural hearing loss. Hearing aids are expensive, and they are not a once-off cost. They need to be replaced every few years. My bowel does not work independently, so my gastroenterologist prescribed a bowel pacemaker drug called Resolor. That's nearly 1500 euros a year. Ironically, the doctors encourage me to work part-time to pace myself and mind my body and my energy levels. I probably would, but I cannot afford it as my medical bills are a part-time job. I am thankful for the care which I have received. I am grateful for my life, for my family and friends, and for my work. I have learned that you can make it work. It's not easy, and some days are a challenge, but most days are a joy. I am resilient.

Now you are just taking the ...

2014 was to bring more drama. I got my gallbladder removed and was diagnosed Coeliac. Dad received his third diagnosis, and we couldn't believe it. His medical team decided that he would not have surgery and rely on Chemo and radiotherapy. He would continue with an immune booster every three weeks going forward. He seemed to be a bit of a pro now. This time he just got on with it, but he also accepted that it was unfortunately always going to be part of his life. He also retired from the Department of Agriculture.

He didn't retire from his videography life because it gave him life in so many ways. He loved it, and he was fantastic at it. He had the confidence and charisma that was required for that job. He was a perfectionist, and he understood his market. Although he knew that people wanted all the small stuff captured, he also appreciated that they might wish for their video the following day to show at their after-party. He put his heart and soul into it, and it showed.

Double date with the big C!

2015 passed with no significant glitches, and it gave us all a chance to catch our breath. It also gave us the freedom and confidence to go on holiday. We went to Disneyland Paris in the summer. It was what I wanted to do for my 40th. I didn't want a big party. I wanted to go to the city of love with Maur and the kids. I wished to put a lock on the Pont des Arts bridge. It was my favourite holiday of all time.

At the end of 2015, I noticed that dad had a swollen stomach. I questioned him about it, and he said that it was from all the excellent wedding dinners. He was trying to convince me that he had put on weight. He even joked about it. The truth was that dad never really gained back his old stature before 2008. He was still a very striking man who commanded a room when he entered it.

After four weeks of nagging him and an actual fight where I got cross with him and accused him of not listening to me, he finally asked me what I thought. I told him straight out that I believed that the cancer was back. There was a pause and sadness in the air. He knew it too, but understandably, he wasn't in the mood to accept it for the fourth time.

He was a fighting man, and he made an appointment with his GP for the following day. It was now 2016. He was referred to his oncologist, Dr. Seamus O Reilly, a man who Dad adored and respected with every fibre of his being and rightly so. Seamus was an amazing man. He saved my Dad so many times, and you got a sense that Seamus saw his patient's battle as his battle too.

Sure enough, it was detected that the swelling in dad's stomach was due to fluid build-up. He was admitted to the hospital, and the fluid was drained. Within days, the fluid returned. His GP sent him to A&E, where he was assessed and moved to the oncology ward to analyse the fluid in his abdomen. He underwent some scans and tests. These would return in days. Following an appointment with his oncologist and several tests, it was announced. Not only did he have cancer back, but on the double. A double date with the big C.

Dad had one tumour in his neck, and one in his stomach, the one in his neck could be treated, but the one in his tummy was a different game of soldiers. He was told to put his affairs in order. Jesus, don't oncologists have a shit job. Imagine having to say to people that they were going to die. How does one ever get used to that? Dad was told that he could try a new drug called Imbruvica if he survived its launch date in October. Although Dad had every intention of grabbing that chance with both hands, he knew that he had the biggest fight on his hands. It was the fight of his life.

That was the first time that I saw my Dad act in panic. He didn't appear upset, but he got into a frantic pace that I had not seen before. First, he started to photograph his video equipment to sell some of it. Then, he began to look at his finances and his company. It breaks my heart to think of him then. My eyes fill with tears as I type this out. *How does one face what he had to face?*

He wanted his news to be kept private because he hated panic and pity, and he wanted as much normality for himself as possible. Ger and I both respected that. Ger was probably the most special person in Dad's life. She was so special to him that it was ok with me to be his number two. He often said that it was because they never complicated things by becoming a couple that they could be the best of friends. I think that in many ways, Dad lost faith in relationships and marriage. But, on the other hand, his life worked perfectly well for him. He often joked that he loved the freedom of not having to answer to anyone, and he could dance with whoever he liked at the dances without stepping on toes or explaining himself. He was never short of a partner either.

He did respect and admire my marriage because he adored Maur. Maur earned his respect and trust and became the best son-in-law that any father-in-law could wish for. He was like a son, a fantastic son. He visited dad every day, waited up at night to carry in his video equipment when it got too heavy, brought up meals and sat chatting with him, and had a laugh.

Dad battled the following months and eagerly awaited news of the miracle drug Imbruvica. Finally, the drug arrived in October. Unfortunately, it was a vicious circle because the treatment saving him was killing him with side effects. His mouth bore blisters, and his throat went dry. His appetite was feeble. In addition, he was losing a lot of weight. People were beginning to notice his weight loss. I hated the way that some people would look at him, and he did too. You could just see it written on their faces that they were looking at a dead man walking. They didn't mean it, of course. They just couldn't help it. He looked very unwell. However, his heart was very much alive, and he faced every day with conviction and pride. He was amazing.

The wonder drug that was to quench all fires came too late. He wasn't strong enough to tolerate its side effects, and that was a cruel blow. It was devastating. But he didn't let that rain on his parade. He carried on. He kept hope in his heart all the time. He reminded me that if we lose hope we have nothing left.

Dad videoed weddings part-time. I mean 3 to 4 per week when I say part-time, so it was another full-time job. But, one that he loved more than any other job, He loved meeting people. He loved having the banter with the couple getting married, and everyone would say that he made them feel so relaxed on their big day.

He was highly efficient and hugely charismatic. His dedication and love for what he did shone out of him like the sun. He would come home late at night after a wedding and stay up into the early hours of the morning to edit the wedding video so that the bride could have it the next day. He kept a master copy of every wedding, show, corporate event, and communion that he ever did, and they lined the walls of his studio in long white rows. I would often have to talk to the back of his head as he would be staring into all his monitors not to be disturbed. He would often happily send you on your way if he was too busy.

I don't think I have ever met or will ever meet someone that loved to be alive more than he did. He packed every minute and never seemed to be under pressure. The only part of his life that he disliked was his treatment days and the fact that they were such a fundamental part of his life and that they would be forever.

Dad grew very weak, but he pushed on. His strength and determination will stay with me forever. It's crazy how cruel and harsh the treatment is for an equally brutal and extreme sickness. He lived to get the drug but didn't live to benefit from it. I had to face my biggest nightmare. Letting go of my dad. I wondered how I was going to do that. But, I learned that love and loss build resilience. As I said earlier, a wonderful person came into my life with every challenge that I faced. This time was no different. However, this time it was two people in the shape of a counsellor named Catherina and one of my work colleagues Tara, who I proudly call one of my best friends.

Letting go

I refer to the next chapter in my life as pure hell on Earth. On the 22nd December, 2016, dad went into Hospital for his usual immune booster. He would be staying overnight in case of any unwanted side effects. I could see the look on the faces of the medical team. Their faces said more than any words could. Dad was gravely ill. They decided at this point that he would come off his drug, Imbruvica. The side effects were too much. His last chance had been used up. There was no hope of him surviving now. However, there was hope that he would get through this next chapter, the most difficult one yet, preparing himself for death. These were the most devastating sentences that I have ever heard in my life.

I brought dad home from the hospital on December 23rd. It's strange the way that some dates keep coming up. On the 23rd of December 2003 I found out that I was pregnant with my first child. It was the happiest day of my life. 13 years later it would be a very different 23rd December. We had to stop in Carrigtohill to collect his script from his doctor. I had held it together on autopilot until I arrived there. I got out and walked to the back of the car, and opened the boot. I cried my heart out. I was devastated. I felt as though I was going to burst open. My two legs were weak under me. My heart was pounding in my chest. My stomach was turning and screaming. My throat became dry, and my breathing was intense. I could not cope. I reached for my phone to call Maurice. I told him that I didn't know how to continue the journey home and maintain the facade of strength that my dad needed and deserved.

Maurice spoke his usual words of wisdom that propped me up a hundred times before despite him hurting too. I got into the car with my children and my dad. I pretended to dad that I had been getting some sweets out of the booth, and he gave out to me for them eating rubbish. He was always focused. The plan was to return to the oncology ward on Tuesday, Jan 3rd, 2017, for his next booster. December 23rd was the last time that I would bring my dad home to his bed. I now had to face my last Christmas with dad, my final weeks *with him in my life, and prepare for the worst days that lay ahead.*

Being resilient doesn't mean that people don't experience stress, emotional upheaval, and suffering. Instead, it means that one can withstand adversity and bounce back from complex life events. Maur is the most resilient person that I know. He experienced a lot of trauma that spanned over a decade. His mum got cancer in 2007, his father-in-law in 2008, 2011, 2014 and 2016, one of his best friends in 2011 and me, his wife in 2012. His best friend's child went to the angels in 2014. One of his closest friends died from cancer in 2012 and his father-in-law in 2017. He still remains patient, loving and supportive. He always gets back up. To me he is the definition of resilience.

Thoughts provoked from reading this story

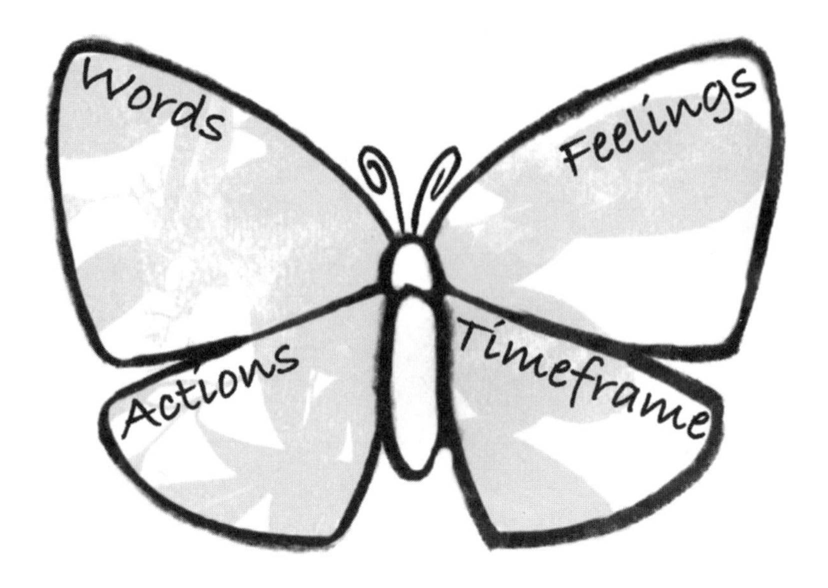

Notes:

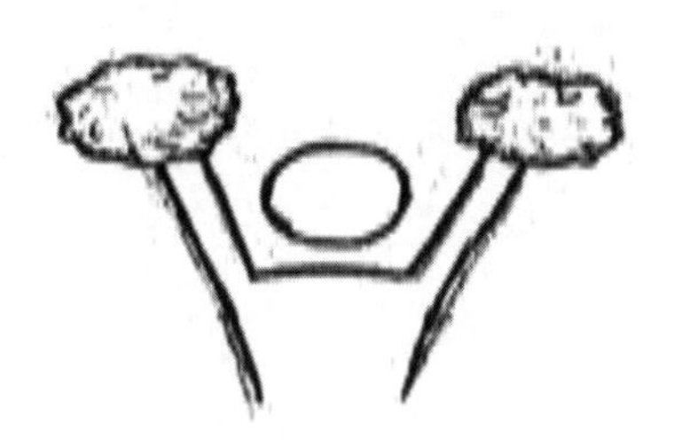

Story 7: Your own worst enemy

'The three C's of life - choices, chances, and changes. Choose to take a chance if you want anything in life to change.'
Maria Gleason. CBT, Maria Gleason.com

'Too many people are thinking of security instead of opportunity. They seem to be more afraid of life than death.'
James F. Byrnes

'The only thing we have to fear is fear itself.'
Franklin D Roosevelt

I have many quotes at the start of this chapter because I needed the most support with the challenge of overcoming being my own worst enemy.

For me, the most significant barrier in my life has been fear. I entirely overthink every decision. I wonder how my choices will affect everyone else but me. I am my own worst enemy. *Are you your own worst enemy? Do you have a warped sense of what your strengths are? Do people compliment you, but you don't listen and don't hear what it means or could mean to you and your future?*

I have learned to become more pragmatic as I get older. I try to stick to the facts. I try to be practical rather than listening to my inner voice and all my fears.

Do you remember when you were a child and played pretend games? Do you remember having high hopes for yourself and confidence in yourself? I remember thinking that I would be a famous actress someday. I would put on little shows at home and force everyone to watch them. *Where along the way do we lose that hope for ourselves?* The hope is that we can be anything we want to be. That walk on the moon feeling. *Does life get in the way? Is it ever too late to follow your dreams?*

I believe that it is never too late to follow your dreams. *If you closed your eyes and thought about what you would most like to do, what would it be? To travel? Change your job? Reconcile with someone? Next, ask yourself, what is preventing you from achieving this? Is it fear? Is it money? Is it time?*

One of my biggest dreams would be to write for a living. I would love it if writing could be my job. They say that if you love your job, you will never work a day in your life. I've always enjoyed my work, and I've always found a way to explore my love of writing in my previous jobs. I loved to write presentations when I was in Eircom. I am always making up and writing stories for the children in school. I believe what is for you, won't pass you. I don't have to be a famous writer. I just have to write. When I thought about it, I realised that I do write a lot. I love to journal. I am writing now. I am doing the thing that I love the most to support a cause that I'd love to help. It's strange how, I can now find the confidence to write publicly when the focus is on something that I feel very strongly about, making more cancer survivors. I hope that what I'm writing is meaning something to someone. I hope that I will write some more books.

I am going to share a little exercise with you. I call it 'Dreams'. It's a 10 step approach. I will give you an example of one of my current 'Dreams.'

1. *What are you dreaming of?*
2. *Why?*
3. *Evidence? Does anyone else in your circle (friends & family) see this as a reality/possibility?*
4. *What are the fears/obstacles? Pros and Cons list.*
5. *Dig deep into those fears – Judge Judy, stick to the facts!*
6. *What needs to be done (to-do list)*
7. *Realistic timeframe*
8. *Who can help?*
9. *What can I do first?*
10. *How will I know that I'm on the right track?*

(1) *What am I dreaming of right now? For me, it's Maurice opening his own business.*

(2) *Then I ask myself - why? Because he is very talented. He dreams of this also, but he is afraid.*

(3) *What is the evidence? Everyone who meets him sees his talent and praises him.*

(4) *What are the fears/obstacles? We made a list of pros and cons. The biggest pro was doing what he loves. The biggest con was worrying about making ends meet.*

(5) *Look at the facts*

- *We are nearly finished our mortgage*
- *I work full time*
- *He has a lot of orders already*
- *He can always get another job if this doesn't work out or he can work part-time while he builds up business.*
- *We can use savings*
- *We can all help him*
- *We have a garage, so no rent to pay*
- *He has all the equipment as he has been collecting it over the years. Get a van*

(6) *To-do list – advertise, put the word out, look for opportunities – making benches for outdoor dining, buying a phone, registering the business, picking a company name, and making plans to save for a van & some wages while we are still both working fulltime.*

(7) *Timeframe – this month we will do ... next month ... by September, he will be up and running.*

(8) *Who can help? We can help each other, Family, Friends.*

(9) *First – make a sign to advertise outdoor furniture as that's what's popular at this time of year.*

(10) *You are on the right track if you are happy.*

I think that we have all been told at some point that we are our own worst enemy. Talk with your friends about your plans & dreams. Get their opinion. Call your bluff.

It's natural to be afraid of the unknown. However, it's important not to look at the whole thing, just the first step then the next. It is like peeling off a plaster slowly and gently. Don't worry about what others will think and say. Try to manage your expectations first, and when you are ready, you can share with others.

I usually have all the groundwork done whenever I am planning a change. Then, after that, I rely on one or two very close friends as sounding boards to bounce my ideas off, and that's pretty much it. I find that sometimes the opinions of others can turn you off your dreams. Sometimes you don't want or need feedback. You just want and need support. It's imperative to explain to your friends and family if you do not want feedback. They mean well, but you don't need their fear and anxieties on top of your own. As I have said before, I believe that you have to teach people how to treat you.

We like to be in control of our lives. Lack of control can be frightening for some of us. However, control is an illusion. Once we get control in one area, it's gone in another. It's like chasing a rainbow's end. The more we try to control a situation we can't control, the more out of control we become.

Please do not underestimate yourself - look back & learn from what you've already achieved. You are unique, and you can do anything that you set your mind to. Put your mind to it. Step outside of your comfort zone. One step at a time. Focus on the small piece of the puzzle in front of you, then the next, and before you know it, you will have created the big picture.

Practice an attitude of gratitude. This will help you see all that you have and give you confidence as you move forward — for example, writing down all the positive things that I have in my life and what I have achieved to date gives me strength and confidence. Try to surround yourself with positive people. I always find that when I'm under pressure, I cannot be with people who are negative or in a bad mood. Behaviour breeds behaviour so if you are in a fragile place surround yourself with strength. This will give you strength. Then you can be there for others when you are strong.

It's important to celebrate small successes. I bought a Pandora Bracelet when I started my teacher training course with Hibernia College. I bought a charm for it every time I passed a milestone on the path — milestones such as teaching practice, an assignment, or an exam. I could see all the charms build up around my wrist. The more that I achieved, the more charms gathered and jingled on my wrist. I kept it sentimental because I love to be sentimental. Each charm had a meaning. For example, when I completed the Gaeltacht part of my course, I bought a shamrock charm. This bracelet was a constant reminder of my vision and my success on my journey to achieving that vision.

I remember when I was working in business markets in Eircom. We were encouraged to take a proactive approach. We were encouraged to constantly look ahead at prospects and anticipate needs and problems, and possible outcomes. It was a very organised approach with many benefits. It created a sense of relaxation, preparedness, and control because you are organised. I remember writing a presentation for an induction course for new sales representatives. I encouraged them to be proactive than reactive. This helps to focus on anticipation rather than reacting, often inappropriately and unprepared.

Be patient. Easier said than done. Patience is said to be a virtue. It is challenging to be patient sometimes. Whenever I am impatient, I try the following self-made strategy:

<u>The Famous 5:</u>

1. Is this urgent? / What's the timeframe?
2. What's the worst that can happen? Be realistic.
3. What can I achieve right now?
4. Who can help me?
5. What do I need to achieve next?

This strategy helps me to organise myself and to be patient with myself.

I remember when the children were young and the holidays would come. I would have a list of things that I needed to get done while also trying to juggle entertaining the children during the school holidays.

<u>Following The Famous 5 strategy:</u>

1. What jobs are urgent? I can list one job each day rather than looking at the extensively long list.
2. What's the worst that can happen? Rome wasn't built in a day. I need to be realistic and pace myself. The only urgent job is – kid's vaccinations, then I put that on the top of my list.
3. What can I achieve right now? First, paint the window sills

as the children play in the garden.

4. Who can help me? My family or friends might take the children to free me up to do the more time-consuming jobs. For example, I could arrange a play date and then swap, and my children could go on a play date then I can get some jobs done. Establish what tasks the children can help me with—sweeping the yard?
5. What do I need to achieve next? Start with what I can do today, then tomorrow, and then the next day.

Focus is essential. It's not easy to be constantly focused, and that's ok. Tomorrow is another day. Strategies that have helped me to stay focused are:

- To-do lists.
- Pictures of goals.
- Vision boards.
- Rewards along the way.
- Targets, deadlines, and reminders on my phone and calendar.
- My diary. I especially love to see all that I have done and to check things off. It gives me a sense of achievement and I find that motivating. Especially when I try to tell myself that I have achieved nothing on a particular day.

When I'm trying to stay focussed on my writing, for example, I book a call with a friend of mine, Marie, I will call her to check in and tell her if I have reached my writing goal. This helped me to stay focused and gives me a bit of healthy pressure.

The 'what if' game can be a dangerous game that can lead to procrastination. There will always be 'what if's'. If you can turn this on its head and instead ask 'why not?' this will help you be more realistic and frank with yourself. Judge Judy. Stick to the facts. Pretend that she is sitting on your shoulder and speaking in your ear. Listen to her. Sometimes you will find yourself retraining for a new way of life - after death, illness, separation, the kids moving out, etc. This is part of life, and with each chapter in life, you have to turn the pages to get to the next chapter. Take your time. Change takes time. It involves learning new skills sometimes, such as going back to work after having a baby. Be gentle with yourself. Try to be pragmatic. Use your common sense and be realistic and practical rather than unrealistic and idealistic.

Life is short. Live it. Live your best life. Don't be your own worst enemy. Be your cheerleader. Go you!

Thoughts provoked from reading this story

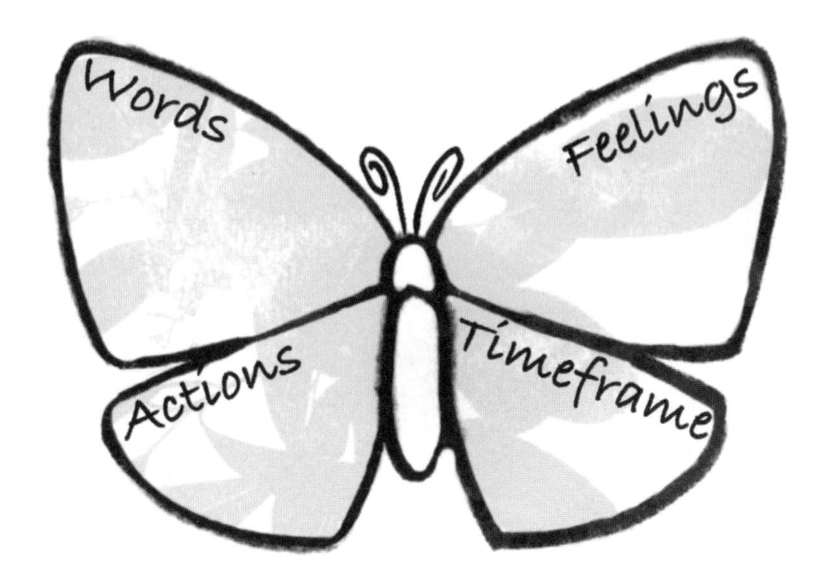

Notes:

Story 8: Accepting The Things We Cannot Change

'When we are no longer able to change a situation,
we are challenged to change ourselves.'

Victor Frankl

There are lots of things in life that we sadly cannot change. Accepting that we cannot change death, is part of the healing process. Holding onto the love that you have around you and in your heart will help you on your way through this tough time. You will be ok in time.

I felt robbed and traumatised after my dad died. We fought the cancer battle so hard for so long, and then he was gone. For nine years, cancer had turned my life upside down and inside out. I didn't know any other way to live. It was tough, looking over your shoulder, all the juggling, the appointments, the waiting, the drugs, the side effects, the hoping and praying, the caring and the worrying. Yet, I have learned to overcome so many challenges while overcoming this considerable void.

Loss is tough, and you think that you'll never be happy again. This was a new feeling for me because I'm naturally a happy and positive person. I was on my knees in every sense of the word. I had to fight to survive it. When I look back now, I am so proud of myself and how far I have travelled. I know that dad is smiling down on me. I am trying to follow my dreams, and I'm putting all my energy into that, being the best I can be for him. It does get better, and you just have to hold on. I never expected to 'get over' my grief, that sentiment annoyed me because it meant getting over my dad's life and his love. Instead, I learned how to accommodate my grief.

I decided to do what is right for me. Your gut will never lead you wrong. Listen to you because you know you best. Hope comes from within. It is not external. Keep trying to have faith in your ability to cope. I set microscopic targets, such as doing something to distract myself for one hour. Then, when I got stronger, I pushed that target out to a full day. After that, I knew what I could do. I knew what I wasn't able to do, and I trusted myself with that. I tried many things such as massage, sleeping tablets, kinesiology, spiritual readers, and lots of crying, lots of hiding away, shopping, and reading. Finally, I went back to my most loved thing to do - writing.

Another thing that we cannot change or control is another person's behaviour, but we can control how we react to it. I have experienced a lot of suffering at the hands of others. Mainly those who have a 'chip on their shoulder' I feel empathy towards them because I understand that they have experienced hurt and pain in the past. However, they have been the most ruthless that I have experienced.

When I was a child, I remember my neighbour saying to me, 'don't stoop so low to pick up so little.' Sometimes you just have to walk away. Some people are unhappy, and when they see another person happy, they want to stop that because it hurts them. The thing is that I wouldn't hurt a fly. I am a very kind and caring person.

Sometimes I wanted to shout at the top of my voice and say, *'I'm hurting real bad, but I'm not talking about it or showing how I feel.'* I don't like to burden people with my challenges, and I want to put on armour. My armour comes in the shape of clothes. I dress up, show up and get on with things.

You never know what a person is going through or how hard they have worked to be happy, be kind. Just because someone looks happy, that doesn't give anyone a right to tear them down. Everyone deserves to be happy. Happiness should be celebrated. If you are not happy, do something about it because you deserve to be happy too. Be careful with people's feelings. Two-way communication is critical. If you can, learn to let go of the past. You cannot change the past. I put an image of the movie Frozen on my notice board as a reminder to let go and not to stoop so low to pick up so little.

Remember!

1. You will learn coping skills. Every day you get up, you will survive something.
2. You will become stronger and important.
3. Expect less, expectations are demanding and exhausting.
4. Set new goals.
5. Reflect on positives.
6. What has happened is in the past, we can bring forward the learnings.
7. No regrets.
8. When we lose something, we value, we underestimate our ability to cope.
9. The most challenging times often lead to the most incredible moments - keep going.
10. We sometimes learn too late the value of Life through seeing the loss and despair created by death and illness.

This leads to acceptance. Remember that the word 'accept' is a verb. It's an active process, one that must be practiced consciously. It may be difficult to imagine, but one day we may choose to accept our emotional or physical pain, our bodies, our complex relationships, or our pasts and never think about it again. If you ever notice a pathway along the edge of a field, the more it's walked upon the more defined it becomes. The same applies to acceptance. We must practice it. Sooner or later, we all have to accept the things that we cannot change. But we can change how we react or deal with it and whether we chose to learn something or not.

I found becoming partially deaf very difficult to accept. About a year after my treatment for thyroid cancer, I noticed that I couldn't hear the TV at the same volume level as I used to. So I started to turn up the volume, and my family and friends commented on how loud the TV was. I began to ask 'what' a lot and say things like 'sorry I didn't catch that' and 'can you say that again, please'? I knew that something was wrong. I mentioned the problem at my next hospital check-up with both the otolaryngologist and endocrinologist. They hadn't heard of a link between my treatment and my newfound deafness, and so I thought that it might just be some kind of a blocked ear problem. Or a lousy hearing phase, so I decided to try to forget about it.

My friends started to notice that I wasn't participating in the conversation. They were waiting for a witty comment that wasn't coming, the truth was I just couldn't hear the conversation, and I hated asking people to repeat themselves, and at that point, they would say, 'are you deaf or what?' not meaning any harm. But the truth was that yes, I was partially deaf.

I was straining my neck to lean in on the conversation, and I started to lip read. I also watched facial expressions to gauge my reactions. I became more removed daily from social interactions. There was a real sense of losing out.

I went to my GP, who checked if my ears were blocked, but all was fine. After that, I bought different ear treatments from the health shop. I took supplements and all kinds of lotions and potions, but no change was to come.

In 2016, not long after dad's final diagnosis, I knew that I had to do something about my hearing. I needed to be able to hear every word at every appointment that dad had to attend. I couldn't afford to miss a word. I saw an advert for free hearing tests at a local high street shop. I decided that I would have a test and see what the professionals thought. Then I could bring my findings to my consultants. Low and behold, I was diagnosed with bilateral sensorineural hearing loss. My audiology report was like a bite on the graph. I left feeling lost. Questions like *'God, am I partially deaf? Will I go entirely deaf? Will I lose my job?'* ran about frantically in my head. I took the audiologist's report to my next consultant appointment. The consultant agreed to refer me to the audiology department of the hospital for a hearing test. Again, he was confident that all was ok. My hearing test came back the same as the high street one. However, I was not diagnosed at this point; instead, I was ushered off to different parts of the hospital for several tests - X-rays, blood tests and an MRI. They thought that I had some audio autoimmune disease. All the tests were clear except the audiology. The conclusion was that I had hearing loss in both ears. I was then advised to go to an audiologist privately and get tested and fitted for hearing aids. At this point, I had lost 18 months of hearing life.

I got tested again at the high street audiologists and purchased my first set of hearing aids. They changed my life instantly. I got my Mojo back within weeks and built up my confidence again. I am still nervous about walking alone because I will not hear traffic until it is very close to me, so I need to be on footpaths, safe roads and preferably accompanied. I do feel vulnerable being deaf. Unfortunately, during the pandemic and the 5K rule, I was limited to narrow country roads and fields.

The new challenge that I faced was telling people constantly that I am partially deaf. It's the spoken word that I find challenging. I can hear background noise with no problem, but it can drown out the spoken word, and some people do not speak clearly, so I still have to ask them to repeat themselves. But overall getting hearing aids has been a game-changer.

I never realised how much hearing aids cost, thousands. You have to buy new ones every few years. I worked out that if I spend between 4 and 5 thousand Euro on hearing aids and replace them every five years when they would be out of warranty or break, that would mean approximately €40K in hearing aids if I lived to be 75. I had to pay for my hearing aids as I don't have a medical card. I decided to take a loan. I would never complete a loan because I would pay it and then start a new one again with every new pair of aids. I refer to this as my hearing debt. I would much prefer a Chanel handbag. The strange thing is, I wouldn't and couldn't lash out €5K for a bag, but then I end up lashing it out for hearing aids. It makes you think, doesn't it? Health is wealth, as my dad always said.

I have a funny 'Joe story' - Dad had some hearing difficulties around the same time as me but was in complete denial. He eventually got a hearing test done, and he was diagnosed with hearing loss and got his hearing aids free from HSE as a medical cardholder. He thought this was great, and he loved to joke about how I had to pay for my aids. It wasn't that he wasn't empathetic, quite the opposite, he just loved to use humour to take the hot air out of a situation.

He spent thousands on his health before he finally qualified for a medical card. His GP and consultants battled hard to support him in qualifying for it a year before his death. He realised that I got my batteries free under my contract. He asked me if my batteries would fit his hearing aids. God, I miss him. I miss all of him.

I got used to my hearing situation, well, that is until the pandemic hit, and we all started to wear masks, making hearing very difficult. Also, hearing in shops was more difficult because of both the customer and shop assistant wearing masks and the presence of clear screens. When I would say sorry *'I am a bit deaf,'* people would reply, *'I know we are all getting a bit deaf,'* it was like they couldn't accept that a young person was deaf, especially when I could speak clearly and it was apparent that I wasn't born deaf. I felt like wearing a badge on my mask, 'deaf.' Lip reading was obviously off the table at this point too. Getting up close to hear better was a no-go with the 2m socially distance rule. The new return to school guideline of double masking was a complete nightmare for me also. Not just from a hearing point of view but also from a vulnerable throat following a critical throat illness. Breathing in my air all day has resulted in many throat infections. The thing that got me most was not the deafness but that I had to fight to prove that I was deaf.

Going forward, I would love to see financial support given to people with hearing loss. I have to teach children in a classroom with all the background noise. A sound system would help greatly but at a cost to me. The government provides sound systems for children with hearing loss. This is fantastic. We have a long way to go to support adults in the same way.

As I've mentioned a few times before, I struggled to accept my fathers' fate.

Words have always been powerful and influential to me. I

love poems, song lyrics, quotes, and sayings, they mean the world to me. Following the death of my dad, I received a lot of compassionate words from people. I also heard many comforting words on the radio, on social media, and television.

Songs that resonated with me were *'It don't matter to the sun'* by Rosie Thomas, *'Fall on me'* by Andrea and Mateo Bocelli, and *'Fix you'* by Coldplay. Whenever I hear them, I get upset, and I am completely moved. They explain through music exactly how I feel. For example, in the song *'It doesn't matter to the sun,'* I am reminded that the sun will still rise and shine down on another day, irrelevant if your loved ones are in it or not. It also reminds me that the world doesn't stop even if it feels as though it has stopped spinning for you for a little while. There will be a tomorrow. I found it very hard to accept that the world would still rotate without my dad, that there would still be a tomorrow, that the moon will just keep hanging around like it's just another night.

I struggled when I saw people living, smiling, laughing, planning, and getting on life. My dad had died. I wanted to shout *'Stop the world.'* I just wanted to get off for a while. Take a breath, process it all. But that was not possible. I had to stay on the world, stay with my day, be a good wife, mother, sister, daughter, friend, aunt, sister-in-law, daughter-in-law, niece, and teacher. I wished that I could just go to an in-between place where everyone was on the same journey, everyone shared the same pain, fragility, and devastation. Unfortunately, such a place doesn't exist. You have to stay in the world and try to keep going in your new abnormal world until the grief is beside you and no longer on top of you. It's pretty cruel when you think of it. It is a huge ask. It is a severe aggravation.

When someone you love dies, you just want to make the pain stop — all of it. The pain is both emotional and physical. Every bone in my body ached for weeks after my dad died. I wanted everyone to know and feel the devastation that I felt. I thought that maybe if everyone felt the same as me, it would help, but in truth, nothing could help. Nothing but perseverance. I wanted the world to stop, even if it was only as a mark of respect for the theft of such a wonderful man. These feelings were beautifully captured in the poem 'Stop All the Clocks by W.H. Auden, read in the movie 'Four weddings and a funeral'.

Four years on. I have moved forward with my grief. I feel so proud of what I have achieved. I am proud that I didn't lose my mind, die of a broken heart, attack anyone, hurt someone with my words and that I kept my family, friends and my job.

Dad, I miss you every day in every way. I know that you are there in a different way. I feel it. I know it.

'I close my eyes, and I'm seeing you everywhere
I step outside
It's like I'm breathing you in the air
I can feel you're there.'

Fall on me - Andrea and Mateo Boccelli

I am weeping for what has been my delight, my dad. What the bereaved need most is the acknowledgment of their pain and sorrow. The death of a loved one is the most profound of all sufferings. It throws every aspect of our lives out of balance and into turmoil.

Love does not die. To grieve is to celebrate the depth of the union. The goal is to learn to face reality and the pain of our loss, say goodbye to the dead loved one, restore ourselves and reinvest in life again. It is hard to let go of the intense connection with the deceased. Although our love will never die, the pain of our loss can eventually dissolve.

'Grief is like a wound that needs attention to heal. We try to face our feelings openly and honestly, express or release our emotions fully, and tolerate and accept our feelings for however long it takes for the wound to heal. Therefore, it takes great courage to grieve.'

The Courage to Grieve - Judy Tatelbaum

Tears afford us a necessary release for our intense feelings. I could burst into tears at any time in those first few months after my Dad died. I still get upset and shed quiet tears. The loss will always be there because the void will always be there. Love does not need grief to support its truth. Love can last in a more healthy and meaningful way once our grief is dispelled.

Death is natural. It reminds us not to wait until tomorrow to do what we mean to do.

'We cannot, after all, judge a biography by its length, by the number of pages in it. We must judge it by the richness of the contents. - sometimes the 'unfinished' are among the most beautiful symphonies.'

Victor Frankl

Each person we love is unique to us. Since grief is so painful and hard to sustain, we tend to push ourselves to finish grieving long before we are ready. Where life was connected to another's, there is a huge gap when the other is gone.

We mustn't expect too much of ourselves since loss makes life feel quite abnormal. Resuming a routine too quickly after a death can be a complicated endeavour. In my opinion, following grief, there are two major tasks to be accomplished. The first is accepting that the death has occurred, and the second is to experience and deal with all the emotions and problems this loss creates for the bereaved.

'For, after all, the best thing one can do when it's raining is to let it rain.'

Henry Wadsworth Longfellow

In truth, I hoped that I would awaken from the nightmare. In my dreams, he was alive. But, when I woke, the hell resumed. So many emotions are tumbling around—shock, numbness, anger, pain, sadness, loneliness, anxiety, fear, and isolation.

I tried to keep busy to avoid the quietness and keep the thoughts at bay for a while, which only brought exhaustion. So much energy is tied up with grief that there is little energy available for action or functioning.

BUT, I will tell you this. You will get there. There is no way around it, and you just have to go through it. Be kind to yourself, be gentle with yourself, and pace yourself. Do it your way. Trust in you. Know and trust that your heavenly person will walk beside you always because love conquers all and that matters to me.

Additional excerpt from Fall on me 𝄞♪

Verse 2:

Soon you will find what your heart wants to know
Don't give up hope, for I know you are close
And all you have ever dreamed wished you could ever be
Is waiting to find you wherever you go
Believe in yourself, every step that you take
Know I am smiling with pride every day
My love will forever be stronger than stone
Don't be afraid you are never alone

Chorus:

Fall on me
With open arms
Fall on me
From where you are
Fall on me
With all your light
With all your light
With all your light
With all your light

- Written by Ian Axel, Chad Vaccarino, FortunatoZampaglione & Matteo Bocelli
- Performed by Andrea Bocelli & Matteo Bocelli

Thoughts provoked from reading this story

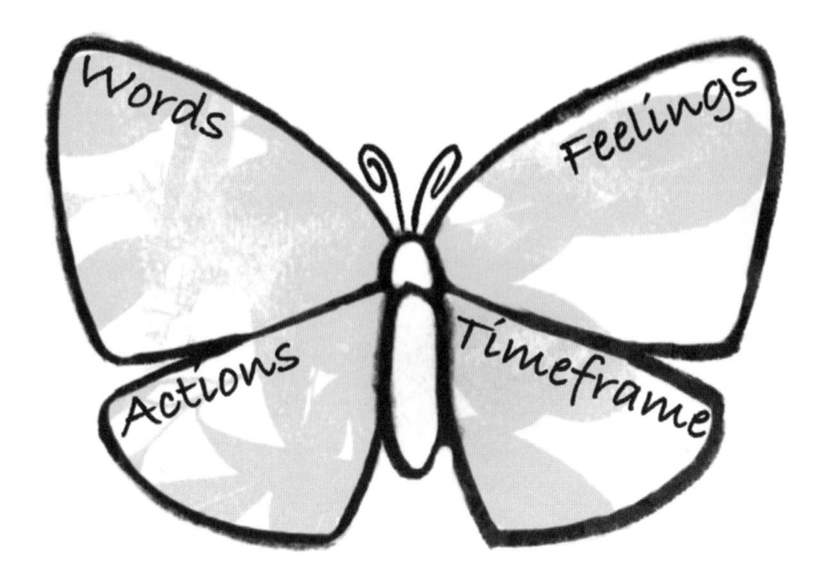

Notes:

Love

Story 9: Perseverance, Finding A Way To Cope

'I have not failed. I've just found 10,000 ways that won't work.'

Thomas Edison

Perseverance is about finding a way to cope with what's in front of you as you try to achieve your goals. Perseverance is about being steadfast in how you do something, despite how hard it is or how long it takes to reach the goal. Of course, it's hard to be steadfast all the time, but in general, it's a good rule of thumb.

When I think of perseverance, the picture that I get in my head is that of a donkey with blinkers. He is moving forward and not looking left or right. He will stop now and then, but he carries on along his journey, not letting anything take from his mission. I was like that when I was trying to become a teacher. I was six months pregnant with my son, Colin, when I realised that I wanted to chase that dream to become a teacher. It's a decision I have no regrets about, but it was complicated. There is a lot to be said about taking one step at a time. This part of my journey reminds me of that game, PAC MAN. I'm hurrying along trying to find my way, and at every bend, there's a challenge. If I stop or choose the wrong path, I'll be eaten.

One day, while sitting on the end of dad's hospital bed, or perched as he would call it, he asked me if I had any regrets in life. For the record, he was not a 'deep' man, but it was just one of those days. I think it's pretty normal to run a check on any potential regrets when you get a brush with 'the big C'. This was our first brush with it, and it was perfectly natural to think about your loved ones and double-check that they are OK, that you did well to provide for them and guide them. We were no different. When dad asked me, I answered no. I am, after all, an over-analyser, so I tend to try to go to bed each night with no regrets. I am pretty good at setting goals and going after them. My challenge, however, is coping through it all. Dad said that he felt it was a shame that I didn't become a teacher. I couldn't believe that one of his potential regrets was about me.

When I was a little girl, I loved to play school with my brothers in the garage at home. I was always the teacher, and they were my students. They agreed to play with me on one condition - that I do their homework. I loved school, so this was no problem. Dad bought me a blackboard and hung it in the garage. Some days when the boys wouldn't cooperate, I swapped them out for teddy bear pupils. I was a bossy thing, and I loved to organise and create, so teaching ticked many boxes for me. When Mam left home I opted not to become a teacher. To be honest, with all the stress at home at the time, I just couldn't get the points required in my exam. I had dropped back from honours Irish to ordinary level Irish. That closed the teaching door for me. I, nevertheless, did what I had to do and have no regrets but it was something that I had always dreamt about doing.

I agreed with dad that day in the hospital that I would think about that dream now and assess how I felt about it. His questioning put some thoughts into my head, and I pondered over it all afternoon and through the night. Questions circled in my head. *Questions such as could I afford it physically and financially? Could I afford not to do it?* At one time it had been a big dream of mine.

I believe that if you want something badly enough, you will make it happen. I just hadn't worked that part out yet. I was six months pregnant, I had a three-year-old at home, I had no job and dad had just got diagnosed with cancer. How, in the name of God could I take on teacher training? To be honest, on top of all the typical considerations, I knew that I couldn't do the Gaeltacht part of the course because I wouldn't be able to leave the kids, Dad, or Maurice for three consecutive weeks.

As I have mentioned previously, extraordinary people have come into my life many times on my journey. Marie has been a massive part of my life since we met in Eircom in the year 2000. We immediately connected, and she has always been a rock for me. She has always had my back and has always wanted the best for me. That is unique and special, something that I do not take for granted. As for many other significant decisions in my life, I rang Marie and planted the seed of me retraining for teaching and asked her what she thought. She immediately welcomed the idea and reassured me that I would be a great teacher. In addition, she gave me her friend's name, who had also changed her career and became a teacher.

The months went by, and dad got well again, and he returned to work. Colin was born, and he was a darling. Mia was thrilled with her little brother, and all was good. Finally, we were ready for the next chapter as a team of five.

They say that if something is for you, it won't pass you. I had heard an advertisement for a college in Cork offering the Leaving Cert Irish program for mature students and repeat 6th years. I also heard an advertisement for Hibernia College's teacher training programme. I decided to phone Hibernia college in Dublin because that course would be my only online and part-time option. They told me the structure of the study, the entry requirements, and the cost.

They also said that families could attend the Gaeltacht, which was music to my ears.

It's true what Maur says, one step at a time. Sometimes, it can be scary when looking at the big picture, so just look at one corner. I got a 'B1' in my ordinary level Irish Leaving Cert 16 years previously. However, Hibernia had a minimum entry requirement of a 'C' grade on a higher-level paper. It was a setback but not the end of the world. I had a lot to think about it, and I weighed up my options. If I were to do the Leaving Certificate Irish again and succeed, it would be a step up on the teacher ladder. On the other hand, if I failed, I would have at least brushed up on my Irish for helping my children with their homework. So I decided to go for it. I called the College and enrolled in their 9-month programme. The entry fee was my birthday present from Maurice. I bought the books, and that was that. I was on my way to what would become one of the most challenging years of my life.

Mia started her educational journey at the same time as I started my teaching journey. She started Montessori, and I started studying the Irish leaving Certificate course. It would be a considerable challenge. The two-year course was put into a nine-month programme, from October to June.

The strength of the mind is a crazy thing. Once you set your mind on something, you can achieve so much. I attended my course every Tuesday and Thursday night. I took grinds once a week on a Saturday from the lecturer, a wonderful man. I didn't listen to a thing on the radio for those nine months unless it was on Raidió Na Gaeltachta. Every spare second that I got, I worked on my Irish.

Every Tuesday and Thursday evening, dad would come up to my house at 5 to stay with the kids until Maur came home from work. I loved that time to myself, even if it was to do an Irish Leaving

Certificate course. I used to be fascinated the following day when I'd ask Mia how she got on with Granddad, and she would say he just read the paper and talked on his phone. My Dad was one of those dads who loved their children from a distance. He was nervous about them.

I used to change and feed Colin before I left so he wouldn't have to do anything while babysitting. Maur would pick up where I left off when he got in. It was only when the kids got older and could have a conversation with dad and do some jobs for him that their relationship flourished. He grew close to Mia, and he used to say, *'Kat, she's so like you when you were little,'* I used to joke back, *'You're only saying that because she can make you a cup of tea'.* Mia used to go up home every night and help her grandad with his DVDs, she used to put each cover page into the DVD sleeves, and they had a beautiful connection. She would come home and say, *'Look what Granddad gave me'* as she waved a ten euro note in the air with a big smile smeared across her face. We used to joke that she was the only one who got money out of Granddad. (only joking dad)

One month into my teaching journey, Colin developed Rubella. He stopped sleeping for more than a few minutes and cried all the time. He suffered from night terrors. I could not believe it. Colin's most prolonged sleep pattern was 17 minutes, and that's the truth. He would fall asleep then wake after several minutes kicking, lashing out, and screaming like he was falling from a building.

I took him to my GP, who recommended several things over a few very challenging weeks. We changed his formula, washing powder, food, bed, nappy brand, night-time routine, bottles. You name it - we tried it. I slept with him thinking that would help. We were desperate to sleep ourselves, but nothing worked.

We made his bedroom into a big cot, we placed a mattress on

the floor and a stair gate across the door. He would still get up and cry until we calmed him. It was never-ending. It continued into the day, and we were going out of our minds. We took him to craniosacral therapists, dieticians, and baby whisperers. Nothing worked. We were desperate. I asked my GP to refer us to a paediatric neurologist. We received an appointment with a neurologist and she assessed Colin.

We had videos and diaries documenting our journey. The neurologist prescribed a light sedative for him, which broke our hearts because we didn't want this for our child. We believed that there had to be another way. We decided to persist. We brought him for late walks to settle him before bed. We took him to the sea air. The only way to rest was to sleep in the car for the few minutes that he would. That was it. I asked the neurologist to run some tests on him—sleep tests, an ECG, and blood work. There just had to be a solution. We were on our knees. We were utterly sleep-deprived.

Maur was trying to work, and I was trying to juggle two children, a house, study and dad being unwell. Mia became exhausted too. It felt as though the walls were caving in on us. The only findings from all the tests were that Colin could not get into a state of deep sleep. Because we didn't want to drug him, we would just have to keep going and hope that he would grow out of it. It was like looking down the barrel of a gun. We didn't know what to do.

I decided that it was best to drop out of my course. I was suffering from motion sickness at this stage. I was so tired that when I walked, I would feel sick. Maur disagreed. He knew that dropping off the course wasn't the answer. He believed that we would work it out. So we thought about what we needed. We needed Colin to sleep, and we knew that there was nothing physically wrong with him. We knew that he knew that he was loved, so we had to wait it out. If that wasn't going to happen soon, we would need some help at night so that we could sleep. In the local paper, we put an advert *'Lady wanted to mind the child in child's own home.'* The next problem was how we were going to pay for it. We decided to use the money I saved for Hibernia, and we took a three-month moratorium on our mortgage. This would allow us to afford to have someone mind Colin in our house two nights a week so that we could sleep. It also covered all the appointments Colin would need in occupational therapy, speech & language therapy, the neurologist, etc. We could afford six months of that, and that would get me over the Leaving Certificate Exam. We would cross the Hibernia bridge when we came to that.

Colin was 11 months old. We got one reply. One reply was all we needed because Deirdre was that one reply. She called me to enquire about the job, and this did put a smile on my face. She agreed to call to see us later that day. We were so excited. The minute I looked at Deirdre, I knew that help had arrived. It was a funny 'interview' because she thought that I was a nurse or in some job that required me to work nights.

I explained that we would be at home too. I'd say that she thought we were complete lunatics. I explained that we needed someone to mind Colin and technically stay up with him so that we could get sleep for two nights a week. She said that she would think about it and left. We were convinced that we would never hear from her again. However, the following day she called to say that she would do a trial night. We were delighted. She arrived at 11 pm and would stay until 7 am.

Being the warm, considerate person that she was, Deirdre offered to do my ironing or any other jobs that I might have. This would be amazing. However, we laughed and explained that she wouldn't have a chance to do any of that while looking after Colin. So we went off to bed, and she went to Colin's room which we had converted back to a little boy's bedroom.

After a few minutes, the show started. Colin was up and crying and lashing out. I found it impossible to stay in bed, but this was a trial, so it was OK to get up and help out. Deirdre stayed the whole night. It was terrific to have another adult around to give a dig out. When she was leaving that morning, she asked if she could have time to think about the job. We were devastated, but we completely understood. We were his parents, and we were barely coping, so we had no expectations of anyone else.

The following day, Deirdre called to say that she would accept the job. She said she couldn't get us out of her head, and she couldn't walk away knowing what we faced each night. I always believed that there were good people in the world. At every turn in my life, I found at least one. Not only did Deirdre do her two nights each week, but she would also often stop by our house on random days and offer to take Colin for a walk or a spin so that I could spend time with Mia or study. We are forever indebted to her and forever grateful to have her in our lives.

My sister-in-law, Susanne, would stop by and take both Colin and Mia for walks in the woods, trips to the playground and of course stopping off for ice cream on the way home. So between the two, we reached our goal of getting through that year, not killing anyone, and getting a B1 in the higher level Irish paper. I wanted to copy that certificate a thousand times and put it on every pole from my house to Cork and back. I had won the lottery of surviving a considerable challenge. If you love and are loved, you will win because love conquers all. It does.

The new problem now was the fact that I had spent the money I had saved for Hibernia on getting Colin better. I went to speak to dad. He advised that I take out a college loan. This would be hard as I wasn't working, so showing how I could pay it back would be a challenge. I also had no savings left. Dad said that he would go as security for the loan. I went to the bank and told them my plan. To my surprise, they were accommodating and supportive. I thought that they would take one look at me and laugh. They did listen. I told them and showed them my successes in my previous jobs to see that I wasn't lazy or wasting their time. They could also see my Leaving Certificate success, and they were acutely aware of how difficult it would be for me, and failure was not an option for me. I had too much to risk. They gave me the money. Onwards and upwards for me, to Hibernia.

Sometimes you are better off not knowing what is ahead because if I had known what was ahead or how difficult it would be, there is no way I would have progressed with it. But as I said, I am delighted that I did it.

My journey of perseverance didn't end there. Little did I know that I would have to face the isolation unit for my radioactive iodine treatment in a couple of years not to mention losing my dad. However, because of previous challenges, I knew that I would always find a way to cope. Coping comes from a place of love, hope and gratitude. You always hope for the best for those you love. Be grateful for all the good in your life. It is said that if everyone put their troubles on a table you would take back your own.

Last Christmas

Dad's final Christmas was a quiet one. He was unfortunate to be missing out on all the dancing. He just didn't have the strength. It was hard to accept that someone who always kept going and rising could not do what he loved.

On Christmas Eve, we went to midnight mass. At communion time, I asked Maurice to get the car and bring it around to the front of the church so that dad wouldn't have to walk too far. When I got up to leave, Dad caught me by the arm and said, '*Kat, I want to see the baby Jesus go into the manger one last time.*' I was frozen to the spot, and the tears streamed down my face just as they do now as I scribe this. The strange thing is that when I looked up, I noticed others were weeping too. Lots of people were thinking sad things. I felt so alone but yet so included, included in sadness. After 41 years of seeing the baby Jesus go into the manger on Christmas Eve with my daddy, this was to be the last. It was a beautiful moment even though my nails were embedded into the seat. It was a beautiful moment in time with him. I was so thankful to have had him in my life, and I thanked God that night for putting us together 41 years previously.

On Christmas Day, as he sat at the table with Maur's parents and us, he said, '*I suppose I'll be pushing up daisies this time next year.*' This was dad accepting his fate and putting it out there for us to accept it too.

On December 29th, dad got it into his head that he wanted to go to Cork to return a jacket that he had received from my youngest brother Kevin for Christmas. My dad and I would collect Ger on the way, and we would meet Kevin and his girlfriend Maria in the city. That was the last time that we would do anything fun together. We had to stop at the bank on the way so that dad could do his lodgements. He always allowed me to put the Santa presents on his credit card. I would give him the money in January, and he would lodge it. My dad was a firm believer that you cut your cloth according to measure, and there were no handouts. You earned what you had. We all knew and accepted this. However, I would often joke to him that I was off to spend money that I didn't have on things I didn't need. It used to drive him crazy.

We had a lovely afternoon in the city. We swapped his coat, and I tried to convince him that he needed new pants and bless him he humoured me in his weak state he allowed me to pull on and off several pairs while he just smiled. I was grateful for that piece of normality. It was a lovely act of love from him. Again I am crying as I type these words. I feel every emotion there was to feel that day.

On our way home from Cork, dad decided to stop at Curry's PC world. Unfortunately, I could not get parking, so dad decided to get out, he instructed me to circle the block. I will never forget the fear that came over me. A trickle of sweat ran down my back. This was crazy and typical of my dad's strength, and he was so headstrong. I always did what I was told, even if I was afraid.

I hated leaving him out of the car. But I did and I circled the car park as I was told. On my third lap, I began to panic. I called the shop and described dad and what he was wearing to the guy who answered my call. I told the lovely man that the 'old gentleman' in the red, black and white coat belonged to me and if anything happened to him he was to call this number. At only sixty-nine years of age, Dad was not old, but he looked old because of all the drugs he had consumed and all the treatments he received over the previous nine years.

New Year's Eve came, myself, Maurice and the kids rang in the New Year with Dad. He even let us take a selfie which hangs in my hall today. Unfortunately, this would be the last photo that I have of my beloved dad. The pain I feel as I type this is real, and I can still smell the smells of that time and feel the pain as if it were fresh. I think of all the Christmas' past. When we were small, our Christmas tree was put up on a milk crate. We felt that it was huge.

It was three feet tall. I remember sitting under that tree and staring up at the lights for hours. I adored Christmas. I now wondered if I would ever like Christmas again and I am still working on that.

I will persevere. I did survive, and I'm still surviving. I found a way, and I moved from hope to cope. My reason to cope was my children. I decided to fight for my life, for my children's sake. I continued to persevere and to stick with it. It takes courage and strength to persevere. I had a desire, a definiteness to be here for my children, and that provided the goal which gave me willpower.

As I write this story, I learn that Perseverance is the name given to NASA's next Mars rover, which is part of the Mars rover mission by NASA's Mars Exploration Program. The Mars 2020/ Perseverance rover is designed to better understand the geology of Mars and seek signs of ancient life. The mission will collect and store a set of rock and soil samples that could be returned to Earth in the future. It will also test new technology to benefit future robotic and human exploration of Mars.

The name was announced by the associate administrator of the Science Mission Directorate Thomas Zurbuchen as part of a celebration at Lake Braddock Secondary School. Alexander Mather, a 14-year-old seventh-grader who participated in 'Name the Rover' essay contest organised by NASA. Mather's essay was the winning entry of the total 28,000 entries submitted by K-12 students from every state and territory in the United States. It was Mather's essay that gave Mars 2020 rover its new identity.

Alexander Mather's essay on Perseverance:

Curiosity. Insight. Spirit. Opportunity.

If you think about it, all of these names of past Mars rovers are qualities we possess as humans. We are always curious, and seek opportunity. We have the spirit and insight to explore the Moon, Mars, and beyond. But, if rovers are to be the qualities of us as a race, we missed the most important thing. Perseverance. We as humans evolved as creatures who could learn to adapt to any situation, no matter how harsh. We are a species of explorers, and we will meet many setbacks on the way to Mars. However, we can persevere. We, not as a nation but as humans, will not give up. The human race will always persevere into the future.

When Mather was asked as to what led him to choose the name, he explained that the Mars mission was just as much about humanity as it was about exploring the Red Planet. He added that the Mars missions require a great deal of perseverance, however, to him, the mission was a lot about being human. The 14-year-old also noted that perseverance is one of our greatest qualities.

Keep going!

Thoughts provoked from reading this story

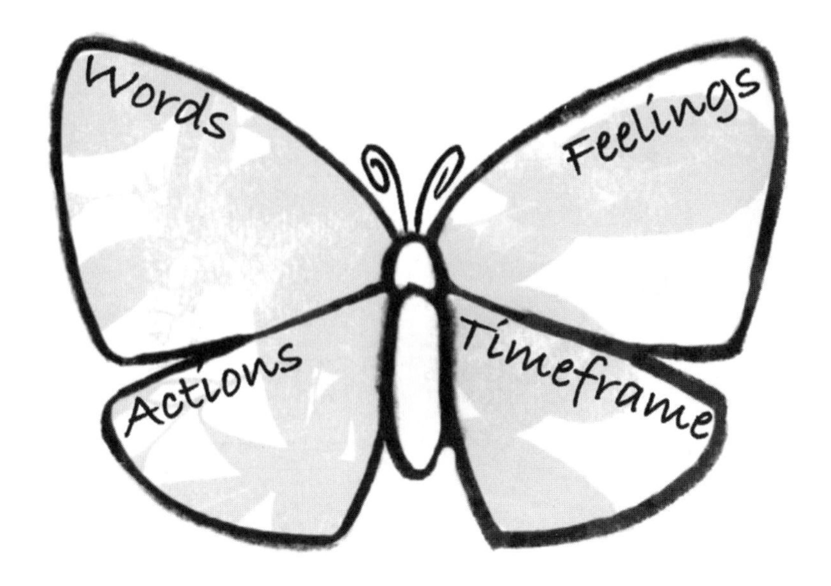

Notes:

Story 10: Stuck in Reverse

'And the tears come streaming down your face, when you lose something you can't replace.'

- Fix you by Coldplay

On January 3rd 2017, as agreed, my dad would return to the hospital. I arrived home at 7am Dad was up and eating his porridge like he did every morning. He was pale and weak but surprisingly bright at the same time. It was a quiet journey as we spoke but a few words. Finally, as we pulled up at the hospital, dad said, *'throw me out at the door Kat and let you head home to leave Moss off to work.'* Dad always referred to Maur as Moss. I watched as he climbed the hospital steps and went inside. He promised to call me when he got to the oncology ward. My phone rang a couple of minutes later. It was him telling me that he was checked in and ready to go. Although he thanked me for bringing him up, he also said that I was a great girl. I felt like a child again. I thrived on pleasing him and making him happy.

We agreed that I would come up late that evening even though he didn't want me to because he hated the fuss and hated being a burden. He never realised that I hung onto those visits with all my heart and prayed that he wouldn't tell me to stay away or go home before I was able to.

Ger and I came back up that night, and he was in good form. He was wearing a little pump that seemed to be connected to his stomach. He told me that this was to administer drugs. We went home happy. The following day we returned to visit Dad. He was his usual bossy self, and I was given jobs like getting the paper, bring home the washing, bring up his razor. It's funny, but when you are that close to someone, you almost become one. I do believe this. I knew that him looking for the razor meant planning a more extended stay than usual. Dad always liked to look his best. He wore bright shirts and jumpers and tailored trousers. He prided himself on his shiny leather shoes.

I was sternly told not to come back in that night, this infuriated me, but I had no choice. He was the boss, and I knew and respected that even though I hated it.

I called him at 8pm to check in, he was in good form but said he was exhausted. At 10pm,I called the ward to check on him. I was afraid to call him in case he was asleep. He would kill me if he thought that I was fussing. The nurse said that he was sleeping.

At 4.30am on Wednesday morning, I awoke crying. I had a horrible feeling - I had a nightmare, and dad was in trouble in it. I had to get up, and I felt awful. I decided to call the ward to check on him as my gut was telling me that something was wrong. The nurse confirmed my fears. She told me that dad was very sick. I announced that I was on my way up, but the nurse insisted that I wait a couple of hours as I would be in the way on the ward, and there was nothing that I could do.

The helplessness almost drove me crazy, and the waiting was cruel. Finally, at 6.30am, I called the ward again. Dad had settled and was asleep. I didn't understand what exactly had happened, but I would be going up to see him in a couple of hours, and I would be put in the loop.

When I arrived on the ward at 9.30am, I turned into dad's room. He was sitting up in bed, but I knew that he was after suffering a terrible ordeal. He said that he thought that he was going to die. However, he went on to explain that he was never as sick as he was that morning.

The nurse was waiting for confirmation that he had picked up the vomiting bug. But, of course, when someone you love is threatened, you run around in your head looking for answers or for someone to blame. *I wondered who gave dad the bug? Was it someone over Christmas? Was it someone at the hospital?* Then the blame made its way full circle back to me. *Why did I bring him to the hospital?*

I just wanted to scoop him up and take him home. But I could not as he was now their property. He was too fragile for my care. I felt so cut off in many ways, and yet I was so connected in terms of decisions that had to be made.

Then the thundering sound of palliative care came tumbling into the conversation like a thunderbolt. Things were moving far too fast for my brain to process, it was like I was on a river raft going down a hill, and the power of the water was pushing me along, almost unbeknownst to myself. A strange strength came over me as I looked at his face. He had to come first. It was not about me. I couldn't believe it when I heard those words coming out of his mouth. *'Kath, they want to talk to you about palliative care'.*

I remember taking a minute then leaning over him as he sat composed in his hospital chair. I asked him what he wanted. I was trying to establish what was best for him, and I didn't want to 'hand him over'. I began to question how anyone could love him like me, look after him like me, know him like me? How did we arrive at this point? I just couldn't believe that they were referring to my dad. I mean, he was like a cat with nine lives. He was a trooper, and he would conquer anything. *How was this happening?*

I did what I had to do, and that was what I was told to do. I went to talk to the doctor about her recommendations for palliative care. It was at this point that I realised how strong the heart is. I could feel it beat slow in my chest. I thought it would stop. But it didn't, it kept beating, and I had to keep listening and reacting.

I wanted my heart to stop. My dad's heart was slowing, and mine was breaking. My chest hurt. I never knew that pain could be this intense. I was frozen with grief.

She asked me to sit down, which is never good, in my opinion. I don't remember sitting, but I remember pressing my feet onto the tiles on the ground beneath me to almost steady myself. She explained what had happened the night before. She explained how sick Dad was and that they wouldn't be able to care for him on the oncology ward. However, over the coming days, while dad was waiting for his home package to be set up, he would stay on the oncology ward.

She warned me that should Dad have a cardiac arrest, they could not resuscitate him because of his bone marrow transplant. I didn't understand, but this was overshadowed by the words 'should he have a cardiac arrest'. This was far too much for me to handle. I was in way over my head. She then said that the decision-making process would now rest with me, his next of kin. This was a very lonely day. It was made extra desolate because the hospital had closed its doors to all visitors except for the next of kin of the critically ill. I was quite literally alone. It was like I skipped a whole series of a box set or an entire chapter in a book.

I left her office and walked down the short corridor to Dad's room. He looked straight at me as I entered his room. He was biting his lip, and his shoulders were raised as he played with his thumbs. This was my only memory of my dad looking vulnerable, and it broke my heart.

'Well, Kath,' he asked. *'All is good,'* I said. I explained that I had spoken with the doctor, and all seemed straightforward. He asked if I was OK with all of this, and I replied that I just wanted what is best for him, and I told him that I would do anything to help him because I loved him. He knew that. He said he was worried about me dealing with him being as sick as he was the night before. We agreed to take things one day at a time, but, to be honest, even that pace scared me.

I left the hospital and went home to collect the kids from school. I phoned my principal to ask for some special leave days. The principal and board of management at my school were highly supportive. I texted my brothers to call a family meeting. It was getting serious now. That night was the start of my sleepless night journey that would be ever-present today.

The following morning I got on the phone to see what advice and support the public health nurse would give me. I then returned to the hospital. When I entered Dad's room, he told me to come over to his chair. He told me that the doctor wanted to talk to me about Marymount. Marymount University Hospital & Hospice provides specialist palliative care services and services to care for dependent older people.

I just couldn't believe it. This was just far too much for me to process. I did everything that I could to stop myself from bursting into tears. I could hear my heartbeat in my eardrums. I wanted to gather Dad in my arms and bring him home. We maintained a gaze at each other for a few seconds it was like there was nothing else in the world but us two, lost in that moment in time.

I struggled to stay focused and to stay strong. Finally, I agreed to talk to them. I leaned over to Dad and put my arms around his neck just like I did as a little girl. I asked him to promise me that if I had to take him to Marymount, he would have to promise me that he would come home too. He promised. That was the day that my dad looked into my soul, just as a new born baby looks into its mothers eyes.

I went to speak to the doctor. They explained that Dad was too weak and vulnerable to be minded at home. They warned me of the risk of him bleeding to death. They asked for a decision. I explained that it was not my decision. I would speak to Dad and revert. They told me that it was indeed my decision. I explained that they would have to wait until I talked with Dad before giving them an answer. I respected that they were trying to navigate a complicated situation, and they have always been extremely good to Dad.

I returned to my Dad's room. He was sitting tentatively in his chair. He said, *'Well Kath?'* I explained that the doctor had advised that he should go to Marymount. I asked him what he wanted to do. He said that he wanted to go to Marymount. I agreed with him that it had made sense and that I could not give him the care he needed despite wanting to so desperately. This still breaks my heart when I think about it.

The rest of that day was spent meeting with Occupational Therapy (OT) and doctors and collecting OT equipment for dad. The following day the hospital told me that there was no bed for Dad in Marymount. He couldn't stay on the oncology ward as it closes on Friday evening. They told me that I could not take him home as if he needed to return to the hospital as an emergency. He would then be in A&E until Monday, which would have been too dangerous for his condition. The only answer was to move him to St Bridget's ward into an isolation room. So at 5pm on January 6th Dad was moved upstairs to St Bridget's, where he would spend the next ten days in isolation. It was a relief that the visiting was opened up a little so that the boys could come up to see Dad. It was hard for them when they were not allowed to visit all along. It was good for Dad to have them visit. He loved the boys and enjoyed their stories.

Those days were what I refer to as 'Limbo.' Dad was on the list to be moved to Marymount, but he was too fragile to move. We were all on the same page now. We just needed to turn the page. Dad needed to go to Marymount. It was the best place for him. It's ironic, however, that he needed to be a little stronger to survive the move. He always reached his goal. This was going to be no exception.

On Monday, January 16th, we got the go-ahead for the move to Marymount. It feels strange to say it, but Dad was excited. I was lonely and afraid. It was all moving too fast, and I couldn't catch my breath, but I couldn't come off the treadmill, I was exhausted. No one can deny it was the right thing to do, and it is about Dad and what is best for him.

I remember that day as clearly as it was yesterday. I got a call to be up at 10am. I washed, dressed, and packed Dad up, and we were good to go onto the next part of our fighting journey of hope. I knelt to put Dad's shoes on. I felt his strong hand resting on my head. *'You're a great girl Kath, and I'm lucky to have you.' 'We are both lucky,'* I replied. Moments like that, I will treasure forever.

The doctor wanted to remove Dad's port. This port was inserted into his chest a couple of years previously to administer his drugs. This port was sore to get fitted. We were hanging onto it for dear life. It was our 'port of hope'. While it was there, we had hope that drugs would come. Keeping that port open meant keeping hope open to us. I was also terrified he would get an infection so he kept the port.

At noon, we were all set and good to go. The porter came with the wheelchair, and Dad sat in as if he was the king of the world. I wheeled him down to the car where Ger was waiting. We bumped into Seamus O'Reilly as we were getting into the car. This was a lovely moment for dad. Seamus asked where he was going, and dad said, *'I'm off to Marymount Seamus,'* Seamus replied, *'That's good, Joe.'* Even though only those few words were spoken, there were a thousand unspoken. I couldn't help but notice how sick and poorly Dad looked when he was outside the hospital. I was taken aback.

We made our way to Marymount and arrived there in about 20 minutes. I went in to declare his arrival. It is one of the most professionally run places I have ever stepped foot in. Everyone was warm, helpful, and supportive. You felt it the minute you went in the door. There was no pity, but yet you felt carried.

I asked the gentleman at reception if dogs were allowed as I had heard that they were. I could not wait to get back to the car to tell Dad that Trix could come in too. Trix is Ger's dog and my Dad's pet. He adored the ground that Trix strut. So we placed Trix onto his lap in the wheelchair, and in we went.

We were sent to St Catherine's ward, room 5. Dad was pleased. The nurse showed him around his room and how to work the TV and bed. I had a great sense of relief because I knew that they would be very good to him. However, I also had a great sense of loss as they would now be doing everything for him. I was just doing his washing. I was not needed as much, and I struggled deeply with that. It reminded me of my kids' first day at school. You know it's the right place for them, you know they have to go, but you still feel so damn vulnerable and scared.

Dad turned to me when he was settled and told me that he wanted me to go back to work tomorrow. I would have preferred if he asked me to walk over hot coals instead of leaving him for such a long spell each day. I wondered how I would find my smile and stamina for the kids. I had no choice. It was what he wanted. I understood that he wanted a bit of normality and me hanging around and not doing my routine was upsetting him. So back I went.

I decided to focus entirely on the job while at school and then go home, sort the kids and go up to him. I did not go into the staff room. I just knew that I couldn't cope with making an effort, I was troubled and lost. Everyone at school is so supportive. I would have made everyone cry, and I didn't want that.

Friday came, and it would be our first weekend in Marymount. Dad was making plans to make a trip home which excited me no end. On Sunday 22nd at 12noon, I was allowed to take Dad home but I had to return him at 6pm. I began to realise that Dad would never come home overnight again. That made me sad. The nurse was giving me a nappy, some relaxing medication, and other drugs for his trip. That went over my head completely. I couldn't understand why Dad needed these things. It turned out he didn't, and we had a great laugh about it after. He loved when he overachieved.

When we got home, I could see how frail he had become. It was so painful to watch someone you love so dearly fight so hard and look so poorly. That day was not what I was expecting. I thought that we would sit around, have a laugh, eat dinner, watch the news, he would read the paper and sit in his favourite spot in the window and take a nap. It was like no day I ever remember at home. It was frantic. He was finalising his affairs. That was difficult to be a part of. It was one of the saddest days that I have experienced at home.

As we made our journey back to Marymount, Dad spoke

little. At one point in the journey, he asked me why I was so quiet. To be honest, all I could hear was noise. It was a noise in my head. Loud noise as my thoughts and fears pounded like crashing waves against the rocks. I made a joke that I was feeling shitty because I was the party pooper bringing him back to Marymount. It's strange how you know in your gut when there's something wrong. That was the last time that my Dad would come home alive. That would be the last time that we would sit by side together in the car. The next time that we would be home together would be for his funeral.

The week that followed, we were just functioning and going through the motions. Dad was growing weaker physically but he was so strong mentally and very much in control. His mental ability far outshone his frail physical appearance. On Thursday, while at school, Dad called me. This was a first. He would never call me at school. I suppose nothing about this time was normal. He wanted me to come straight up after school to meet with his accountant. I promised I would. He was funny. He spent weeks trying to get rid of me and keep me away from Marymount, and here he is looking for me to come straight up after school. Even though I knew that it wouldn't be a tea party, I was still happy that I was cordially invited and equally delighted that I was needed again. I arranged for the kids to be minded, and off I went.

When I arrived at the hospital, Dad's accountant was already in Dad's room with him. He was a lovely, kind, direct sort of a guy who suited Dad. A no-bullshit kind of guy. Sadly he too died from cancer two and a half years after Dad. The purpose of the visit was disclosed immediately. *'Kath, I'm retiring from my company today.'* He declared. He then went on to reassure me that he wouldn't keep me long. Little did he know that I wanted to set up camp there. He told me that the best decision at the moment is that we close the company. I explained to him that I wasn't ready to lose everything at the same time. I suggested a one-step at a time approach. I promised him that I would honour all work on the books, and then decide what to do with the company going forward, which brought a smile to his face.

Dad retiring meant that I would become the only signatory on the company. I witnessed him sign out of a company that he had built from the ground up. A company that took him through a divorce, single parenting, and cancer. Now he had to let it go just like I had to let him go. It was sad. It was tough. Then just like that, it was done.

He told me that I needed to go to the nearest AIB bank with his signed letter to declare his retirement and list me as the sole signatory on the company. This was all new to me. But I would do it step by step and day by day, and Ger would help me. She was fast becoming my right arm, just like Maur was for me at home. The bank staff were friendly, and they helped me out and got things sorted pretty quickly. But, deep in my heart, I wondered how I would face the challenges ahead. So many horrible things lay ahead - Dad's funeral, living without him and training myself to live without him, trying not to crack up, running and then closing his company. As the executive of his estate, I would have to oversee his entire will. Alone. It was a mammoth task, and I was terrified.

The following night, while visiting Dad, one of the nurses called me aside to warn me that Dad would get weaker and weaker from now on. She told me that he would have about two weeks left. I knew we had only days left. So I called his brother and sisters in Galway to invite them down.

I hate the way you have to act like the dying are already dead when they're in their final days. But I suppose people want the opportunity to say goodbye. That was something that I just couldn't do. I still hadn't said goodbye. I will never say goodbye. He is still alive to me today, but differently. I feel his spirit guiding me every day.

Sunday came, and it was busy. I spent pretty much most of that day in the canteen meeting and greeting people. When I finally got to see Dad, he was utterly exhausted. This was so hard. I just found it so difficult to step back.

Tuesday was the start of Dad's anger towards his death. He was very restless. He started to dip his toe into the funeral talk. '*What funeral directors would you go to Kath?*' to which I replied, '*Hyde's dad because you worked there part-time when you were trying to buy your house, and we went to school with them.*' '*That's perfect,*' he agreed. Then he got cross and said, '*Don't you go and have a circus with a big limousine for my funeral.*' I joked with him. '*As if I'd spend that kind of money.*' We were frustrated by the situation which we found ourselves in. We were devastated.

I decided to tell Mia and Colin that Granddad is dying. They are naturally devastated and wanted to see him. We agreed that they can visit the following night.

On Wednesday, the anger intensifies. I appear around the corner and into his room. He is not happy to see me. He is cross. He asks why I am not in school. I tell him that I'm not able to go. He tells me to cop myself on. He wants me to be strong, but I'm sick of being strong. I don't want to be strong anymore. I want to cry in a ball in the corner or scream from the top of my lungs.

I raise my voice. I tell him that I'm not going to celebrate him dying. I am sad and angry. I feel I'm being robbed blind, and there isn't a damn thing I can do about it except suck it up. He told me to go home, and he will tell me when he's dying, and I could come back then. He shouted at me. I leaned over, kissed him on the cheek as the tears rolled down mine. I left his room with the heaviest of hearts. Ger was with me. Thank God. I thanked God for her and Maurice a hundred times during that time.

I cried as I walked down the corridor, the saddest corridor in the world. I could see and feel the pain and the love in that corridor. Everyone had a strong appreciation of how short and valuable life is as we tried to drag as much as possible out of our final days as a family. I sat in the lobby, unsure of what to do. Dad upstairs and I downstairs. A million miles apart. I was approached by a nurse who was aware of what was going on. She explained that this behaviour is expected with the closest people. It's when love meets anger because life is meeting death.

She explained that he doesn't want to go. I'm overcome with grief. She goes on to express her concern for my mental health. I try to reassure her that I will be fine. She explains that Dad told her that he worries about me and how I'll cope after he dies. I could have killed him there and then. *How could he doubt me?* I look back now, and I understand I would be worried too. If it was Mia and Colin facing it with me. He wasn't far off, to be honest, because I did find it incredibly difficult.

I told the nurse that I was visiting a counsellor. I had decided to talk to Catherina in October simply because I couldn't accept losing my Dad. I had a connection built up, and she would help me with my grief. The nurse advised me to go home. I couldn't physically leave. Finally, Ger convinced me to go back to her house to have something to eat. It's amazing what little food you can survive on when you're going through hell. I had lost a stone of weight which was a lot for someone who weighs 8.5 stone. My weight loss worried Dad, and I'm sure that I must have looked broken despite all my acting.

While at Ger's, Maurice called to tell me that he will bring Mia up to see Granddad. I asked them to collect me, and we travel together. Dad is furious when he sees me. He reminds me that he told me to stay away. We are only there 5 minutes, Maurice is making small talk with him. Dad and Maur had an incredible bond. Dad had a great time for Maur. This was reciprocated because Maur had a real soft spot for him. They were important to each other. I will always be grateful for how good Maur was to Dad. He was amazing.

The following day, while I waited downstairs, banished from Dad's room. I watched my brothers take turns to visit him. I felt so close to him but yet so far. I was so frustrated and angry with him. All of a sudden a nurse approached me and told me that my father wanted to speak with me immediately. A wave of panic flashed over me. I climbed the stairs three steps at a time. I entered his room. He reached out his arms, and I travelled to his bedside and knelt on the floor beside him. He started to speak.

His voice was strained, and he was difficult to understand. He kept uttering the words *'Sorry Kat'.* He rubbed my face and held his weak hand over my right cheek. Those were his last words. I whispered, *'It's OK, Dad, I love you, you can go now,'* and that was our last conversation. At that point, I thought that I would never survive the pain. It was immense. I was stuck in reverse.

When Dad died, a numbness fell over me. I was exhausted, heartbroken, and in shock. I fainted. Dad died at ten past ten on February 4th. Ten out of ten was how I always saw him, so it made sense that he died at 10.10am. I have always suffered from low blood pressure and have been fainter since I was a child. But on this occasion, my blood pressure wasn't down, it was through the roof. The faint was me putting up my white flag. I was done. I had nothing left to give. I got over the faint but not the death.

So much is expected of you in the hours and days after the death of your loved one. I was my fathers' next of kin, the executrix of his estate, and a director in his company. Not to mention the elephant in the room, his devastated, grieving daughter.

I left Marymount that morning, having been there every day for the past 16 days. I had to leave my Dad behind and go and do something that I was dreading with every fibre of my being, arrange his funeral. Everyone seemed to have a question for me. I found that you go through the motions of the funeral in a sort of gliding, numbing way.

There are always good people to carry you or prop you up when you need it. There are always people who will challenge you too, but that's life, I'm afraid. You rise above that because you have more important things to tend to.

When the funeral is over, you have the tidy-up. I call this the significant return. You have to work out who brought what and who to return what to. Funeral bills need to be paid. I remember going back to my house after Dad's funeral. I am house proud, but I hadn't done anything above the essential things in my house for at least two weeks. The quietness was eerie. I put some order on my home and caught up with my children.

There was no way that I could have hid the gravity of my loss from my children. I was a stone lighter in weight that I couldn't afford, my face was drawn, and I looked broken-hearted. My eyes were red and sore from tears, I was exhausted and lost, and they could see that. It was a difficult time for them. But, we all tried our best to get through it.

The next challenge was registering his death, informing his employer to stop his pension, cancelling his life insurance, and contacting his solicitor. I decided to pace myself and do the priorities.

I would leave utility bills and other correspondence for another time. I waited for each one to send a bill or invoice, and then I informed them one by one. It was less overwhelming.

I had only one week off work after my Dad died, and that included the day of his funeral. This was because I didn't have any sick days left due to my surgeries and consultant appointments. I could have taken unpaid leave, but I couldn't afford it.

I returned to work. It was a distraction, but it was hard. I love the children, but I needed so much patience and was conscious that I would appear unhappy, so I tried extra hard.

I stayed in my classroom during breaks because I couldn't find the strength to pretend to be OK with my colleagues, and the last thing that I wanted was to upset anyone. So I kept my head down. Maur bought me a small fridge and a kettle to keep by my desk for break times. I had amazing friends who visited me, especially Tara, who brought me a takeaway coffee every morning. I will never forget that of her.

I used my break times to write to-do lists and make calls from Dad's phone to run his company. I had decided that I would honour the work booked in and then close his company. That was a real challenge. I didn't know a lot about his business. I had no experience with videography. Dad had a great cameraman, Gerry, who would help him with double booking, so he could do all the video work and the editing, which was great. I managed the phone and the deliveries, invoices, and orders and met with the accountants. I did that for six months, and then I closed the company.

That was also a challenge. I never closed a company before. It was another part of my Dad that I would have to let go of. I wish that I could have had less to do. It was excruciatingly difficult to juggle everything. I was still a wife and mother, a full-time teacher, and I had a home and a company to run. I had all my duties to carry out as the executrix of Dad's estate. I was grieving to hell and back. I was also functioning on ill health, and my grief was so painfully intense. It was the heaviest weight I'd ever carried, and not for one minute of any day did I think that I could do it.

I was waiting to fail or drop, to be honest. I hated that time. It still haunts me. It still angers me. I still feel robbed by that journey, and I wouldn't wish that on my worst enemy. To be honest, I am only alive today because I am a mother. I love my children. I couldn't put more grief on them. I appreciate that it sounds so ungrateful of me. I had the most incredible husband, two exceptional children, fantastic friends, a beautiful home, and a lovely job. That will just tell you how hurt I was at that time. I had enough of the pain and I wanted it to go away.

On my dad's first anniversary, I had achieved a lot. I was still here fighting away. My grief was still weighty. I had read several books about the grieving process and how long it would last. I couldn't see how it could get easier. I yearned for the day that grief would be beside me and not on top of me.

Thankfully Maur and Ger had dragged me through the year, and the kids were doing well. I had booked them both into play therapy again. I found this beneficial following my cancer diagnosis, and I would highly recommend it for childhood trauma. I was attending counselling weekly. Dad's estate was nearly completed. His company was closed. I managed to get through the school year with no carnage.

I was heartbroken that I couldn't go home. My Dad was gone. The only way that I could see him again was when I would die. The reality that we could not all be together again was devastating. But it was the reality and something that I couldn't change.

Year two began with me job sharing, which gave me a slight

chance to catch my breath. However, it was still busy as I was still working on his estate. It seemed that everyone was encouraging me to go out, have fun, live a little, but I was just not ready. In my writing at that time, I noticed that my biggest struggle was being so close to home and not going home. I struggled to go out to my clothesline because his silhouette was missing in the window next door. I needed a break from Knockgorm. My head needed a break, a change of scenery.

My friends organised a trip to Dubai. I had never been away from my children unless I was in hospital myself or with Dad. I knew that I needed the break. Thanks to my husband, the trip went ahead. I will say that I am forever indebted to them for organising it. That trip changed my life. It gave me back a life that I wanted to quit on. I laughed for the first time in a long time. It was the first time I could remember that I was only responsible for myself for as long as I could remember. I felt so free and so alive. I was surprised by how much good the trip did for me. I was terrified that I would have a panic attack over there or worse, that I would cry the whole time and ruin the trip for my friends but I didn't.

Dad had left me some money in his will. I decided that this would go towards my children's education. I bought a kitchen table. Dad was a year in heaven when I replaced the kitchen table. I hadn't been able to sit at the old table because I missed him sitting across from me. Buying that new table helped so much. The old table just broke my heart. The minute it came into the house, I started to eat properly again like my old self. I continued to invest in the house to see his stamp all around me — a fresh start.

I wrote a Mental Health To-Do List so that I would stay on track:

1. Develop perseverance
2. Don't be afraid to fail
3. Growth mindset – do a little extra every day
4. Take risks
5. Understand resilience
6. Build a network of support
7. Set clear boundaries
8. Exercise regularly
9. Keep goals in mind
10. Perseverance is key to a successful life, keep persevering long enough, and you will achieve true potential
11. You can do anything when you set your mind to it
12. Take action, be persistent, and have the courage to face your fears
13. A sedulous person works hard and doesn't give up easily
14. Let experience be your most excellent teacher
15. You've got this
16. Focus on what you want and what you need and journey towards getting it
17. Make hay when the sun shines
18. Persist - willpower - definiteness in purpose
19. Keep going even when rejected
20. What we think we deserve versus our ability to get to go out and get it- continue to invest in you - persevere with your resilience

I was stuck in reverse for a while. I am now moving forward. I am looking forward and I will keep going. I have mentioned previously, the power of words. I love the song *Fix you* by Coldplay. Maur gifted me this song after my dad's funeral. He so desperately wanted to fix me when I was stuck in reverse.

This song deals with true love, helping someone in your time of need, and learning from your mistakes. Coldplay lead singer Chris Martin hasn't spoken about the specific inspiration for the song, but it could be directed to his former wife, Gwyneth Paltrow, who was dealing with the death of her father in 2002. In USA Today, Martin did say where the song started: 'My father-in-law Bruce Paltrow bought this big keyboard just before he died. No one had ever plugged it in. I plugged it in, and there was this incredible sound I'd never heard before. All these songs poured out from this one sound. Something has to inspire you, and something else takes over. It's very cloudy.' - Songfacts.com

Excerpt from Fix You – Coldplay

And the tears come streaming down your face
When you lose something you can't replace
When you love someone, but it goes to waste
Could it be worse?

Lights will guide you home
And ignite your bones
And I will try to fix you
And high up above, or down below
When you're too in love to let it go
But if you never try, you'll never know
Just what you're worth

On Father's day 2021, I put the following piece up on my Instagram page. I had written it in 2019 on a lantern for my dad for the Irish Cancer Society Relay for life fundraiser.

My Dad

He taught me right from wrong when I was three and that some things in life would just simply be.

A shoulder to cry on, a strong ear to rely on, advice I would follow 'til all my troubles were gone.

He told me to change the things I could change and showed me how to face all the things I found strange.

He taught me that sickness was a battle to fight; at the end of the tunnel, there would always be light.

He taught me that the grass isn't always greener on the other side, so follow your heart with dignity and pride.

He taught me not to waste energy on giving out, and that only positive words should come out of my mouth.

He taught me to be kind, sweet, patient, and caring, and a life worth living was a life worth sharing.

He taught me that a cool head meant a dry pants, and how he owed a lot of his joy to his love of dance.

He taught me to cut my cloth according to measure and that love was something, always to treasure.

He taught me to stand on my own two feet, and success with hard work was hard to beat.

He taught me to be independent, resourceful, honest and true, in every single thing that I would do.

He taught me to gather the facts before I decide, so that with a clear conscience, I could reside.

Death left a heartache that no one can heal, but his love left memories that no one can steal

You always helped me to find a way, a gift I will forever treasure. Rest in peace Dad.

Thoughts provoked from reading this story

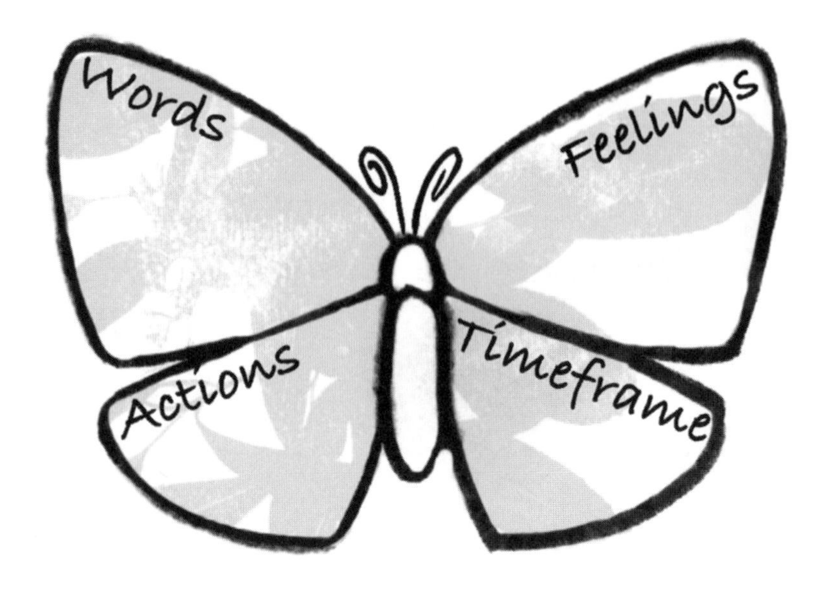

Notes:

Today?

Story 11: Positivity and Being Real

'The problem is not the problem. The problem is your attitude about the problem.'

Jack Sparrow, Pirates of the Caribbean

'The greatest discovery of all time is that a person can change his future by merely changing his attitude.'

Oprah Winfrey

Most days, I feel optimistic and grateful for all the good that I have in my life, but I sometimes feel angry for what I have lost and how much I have suffered over the years. It is essential to embrace the joyous days and get through the less positive ones as best we can. Getting through those days begins with accepting that they are here. Being kind to ourselves on those difficult days is very important. Talk to someone who cares about you. Honestly, you know yourself best, and you know what you need. Make sure that you ask for what you need.

I noticed that sometimes when I was feeling low, I knew that speaking to a close friend would help. But, sometimes, I allowed my inner critic to interfere and convince me that I was just a burden or a liability, and so I didn't call. I know that I am not always going to stay positive, but I am trying. If I come to a time when I can't be positive, I know where to find a positive person. Sometimes the most positive thing that I can do is to do nothing and just be.

I still have moments whereby my eyes fill with tears, and I feel overwhelmed. I know that if anyone asks me if I'm okay or even notices that I am not myself, I will tip over. I just want to be with myself and get through it. Life is tough. Change is tough. But you are tough too. Sometimes it helps to say that you feel overwhelmed and other times, it just doesn't. You do know yourself best. It's important to know that you can reach out. We must remind our friends and family that they can reach out and that we are here for them. A little reminder could change someone's day.

Positivity can help one to heal from one's past. When planning my wedding, I started to think more about having children, which led me to think about them not knowing their maternal grandmother. I decided that the right thing to do would be to find my mum and invite her to my wedding. I hadn't seen her in over ten years.

This was challenging because it was difficult to find her, and I knew it would upset my dad. However, we spoke about it, and he accepted my decision to invite her. Back then, the bride's mother sat with the Father of the groom, and the groom's mother sat with the Father of the bride, so that was the meal covered. It all went fine. It was difficult in places and awkward at times, but it was okay.

Because we got married on the National Day of Mourning, September 14th, 2001, following the tragedy of 911, it took a lot of focus off my parents and onto that sad time in America. Our honeymoon in New York was cancelled, and we would have a very different wedding day but there were more important issues at play.

Positivity can help you cope with life. Positivity can change your life. I don't mean going around pretending that all is well when it's not. Rather be honest with yourself and others. Positivity in this instance would be accepting that all is not well today. Do as little as possible because you need to slow today. That's the positive thing to do for you. Tomorrow is another day.

How to make a positive change? First, you need to think about what you would like to change. Then, think about what needs to change, who could help and what you must do. Identify the obstacles.

Thinking and acting negatively can quench your light, and it's even more critical that you don't let others dim your light. I find a daily analysis helpful. I establish what is giving and what is taking from my life; this will help me find solutions and be patient. Be kind to yourself.

Take one step at a time, do the next right thing, and you will feel happier and more content and in control of your life. When you're happy, you release endorphins, a feeling of well-being. In time you will begin to build positive belief in your ability. You will see challenges as opportunities, and when you see possibilities, you will be motivated and confident to take those opportunities.

I remember when the opportunity arose to do a testimonial for Vhi Healthcare. Of course, I was nervous, but I embraced the opportunity, and it was a fantastic adventure.

I hate being partially deaf, but I have to embrace it and get used to it. One day at school I was chatting to a boy who had a physical disability. He was agitated that he couldn't run with his friends. My heart broke for him. Then I thought about the Power of Positivity. I needed to be a role model for him. I told him about my hearing loss. I showed him my hearing aids. I explained to him that I had to teach all my friends and family how to deal with my hearing loss. I explained that I needed people to be patient with me because I will not always hear what they say. Sometimes, I might be in danger when I walk because I cannot hear traffic, so I need help. He was absorbing all that I was telling him. He was identifying with me. He was thinking about and relating his situation to mine. Then he said. *'Okay, Múinteoir, I will talk to my friends and tell them to slow down for me.'* My heart melted for him.

He taught me something that day. He taught me that it's okay to be different. He taught me to be honest and open about my disability, to embrace it and to ask for help when needed. He helped me to relate to him, and that is what life is all about - relationships and being able to relate to one another.

I remember when I went for a promotion at my first big job. I was a sales representative, and an opportunity arose to be a team leader. I was determined to get the job. I had no experience in management. Well, no experience on paper. I had had a lot of experience from home, which I related to in my interview. I explained the cleaning systems and organisation hacks that I had put in place to motivate my brothers to tidy up after themselves and help out around the house. I sold my brothers the idea of teamwork, and it worked, and I had positive results. There were no clothes washed and no food cooked when it didn't work, so the motivation was clear cut and simple. It's the same in business; everyone has a price. You just have to find out where they are coming from and meet them halfway. I then proceeded to continue my career development and eventually head a department.

The goal is to eliminate your life of negativity. If someone is toxic, walk away.

Eliminating the nonessentials makes life less complicated and more simplified. I think that it is crucial to be kind to others even if they don't deserve it. Then, what goes around comes around, and kindness will come back to you. It's also important to show your children that it is essential to be kind to others. You never know why someone might need that little bit of kindness from you.

If you can build support networks, this will act as a cushion for you when you need help. I know this might sound a little strange, but it is essential to collect people as you go through life. I believe that people are put in our paths for a reason.

Everyone that we meet teaches us a lesson. Sometimes, it can be a lesson to walk away and take the learnings to prepare you for a better future. My dad used to say to me, '*Kath, I don't mind you getting a kick in the arse, but if you bend over for a second kick, you deserve it.*' On a positive note, you can't lose. You either gain a friend, or you learn a lesson.

Being positive and gentle with yourself is so important. Life is tough, and it is short so go easy. Make mistakes but don't beat yourself up about them. Learn from them and move on. I encourage you to celebrate little successes.

I also think that it's essential to teach people how to treat you. If you are always available and always say yes, or you never stand up for yourself, you create a pattern. Watch how people treat you. It's okay to speak up for you. You can have your say and be gentle with your message at the same time.

I believe that our perception of reality can change our facts, how we understand, interpret, and regard what we are experiencing. *What is influencing our perception? Is it past experiences? Rumours? Lack of experience? Or fear?* When we dig into the feelings and emotions, we can better understand each situation and make more informed decisions.

My dad always said *'keep a cool head and dry pants'* i.e. don't waste time stressing. Put your time and energy into living. If you cannot change a situation, then just step away. Worrying will never help. He also said, *'the far off hills are green.'* Hope will bring opportunity.

I enjoy writing a list of compliments and accomplishments because it grounds me and raises me up. I find that this exercise is a worthwhile investment in my future. If, in the end, I am having a bad day, then I will bring out my notebook and remind myself of all the positive things that others have said, and I have achieved.

It is important to have perspective. Look at the whole picture. Take your time before you speak or make a judgment or a decision, especially if someone has hurt you. Don't react. Try to be better than what's thrown at you. Gather your thoughts and then respond rather than react.

When I am struggling to find the positives in something, I try turning on the gratitude attitude. This involves writing down one thing every day that I am grateful for, 365 things per year. This activity can get you thinking positively.

Sometimes when you hear a sad story, you can immediately realise how lucky you are yourself. Turn a negative into a positive. There is nothing like a heart breaking story to make one realise how full one's heart is.

It is crucial to understand and identify what toxic positivity is. I experienced this quite often but didn't know it until I recently watched a cognitive behaviour therapy video.

If you tell someone about a problem you are experiencing, and someone dismisses it with a patronising comment, that's toxic positivity. For example, if you say that you had a terrible day at work and someone replies with *'ah sure, aren't you lucky to have a job, don't you get great holidays.'* That's toxic positivity. The problem with toxic Positivity is that it dismisses your valid emotions and tells you that you're not allowed to feel negatively about anything.

While I believe that you can try to be positive, I also think that it should not be at the expense of suppressing your feelings. Be honest with your feelings. Be realistic and accurate. Say how you feel in a balanced way. If it's shit, say it's shit. Allow others to say it's shit You should feel safe to say how you are feeling. Not everything has a positive slant, like death, for example. So you can say positive things about the dead but not about the loss.

Don't compare or use toxic positivity. Just listen and empathise. Agree with the person; if you don't agree, then say nothing.

I remember complaining/venting to someone about the cost of my new hearing aids, which were €5K, they said, *'Aren't you lucky to be able to get them and improve the quality of your hearing.'* I mean, Christ! Yes, I'm happy they are available, but I was 40. I'd like to hear for free, and I would also have liked if cancer didn't take my hearing. I hate that I will have to pay €5K every five years for the rest of my life to be able to hear.

I wouldn't mind, but these people know that I don't qualify for a medical card. After all, I work full time. I can't afford to work part-time because of my medical bills. Why couldn't they just say, *'Jesus girl, that's shit, I don't know how you manage.'*

Emotions aren't inherently positive or negative. They simply point us in varying directions throughout life. It is critical to express all the feelings that can negatively impact our bodies, minds, and spirits. Toxic positivity is undermining and dismissive of the reality of a person's experience.

How to Avoid toxic Positivity:

Instead of: Just stay positive.
Say: That must be hard.

Instead of: Everything happens for a reason.
Say: I'm sorry you're going through this.

Instead of: Things will work out / look on the bright side.
Say: This just really sucks right now.
Is there anything I can do to support you?

@avamariedoodles

Another comment that I hate is when people tell me that time will heal. I know that they mean well, but that sentence drives me to distraction. Time won't help. Time will allow me to process and accept, but it doesn't help.

Gratitude attitude

I have found it very helpful and healing to be thankful for what I have. We tend to look over our shoulders and notice something that someone has that we don't. What we fail to realise is that we cannot have it all.

Life is a journey. We are each at a different stage on the trip. I might look at someone who has excellent health and feel jealous, and they might be looking at me and seeing my lovely family and feel jealous.

We need to stop looking over our shoulders and start to look at what's in front of us. My dad used to remind me that the grass isn't always greener on the other side. Gratitude comes from within.

It can be challenging to feel grateful all the time, and some days it can be even more challenging. It's ironic that on the tough days is when you need to be most grateful to help you cope with your day. I found it helpful to start with one thing per day. Set a timer on your phone and write one thing that you are grateful for that day. These will build and grow to hundreds of things when you get into the habit of and train yourself to think about gratitude. You might find it helpful to gather positive quotes and affirmations.

'I am thankful to all who have said no to me, and it is because of them that I am doing it myself.'

Albert Einstein

'The way I see it if you want to see the rainbow, you got to put up with the rain.'

Dolly Parton

'Don't be afraid to give up the good to go for the great.'

John D. Rockefeller

I've loved a lot about what that I've done. I love to write and share and help others based on my experiences. The strategies and tips that worked for me and helped me through might help others too. I hope that its positivity will make someone smile. Together we are stronger.

This book covers work and life experience covering sickness, grief, changing career, and moving from private to the public sector. It's not a book that you read and pass on but one that you go back to and refer to wherever you are on your journey.

If you believe you can you probably will, for success begins with a person's will; it's all in the state of mind. Keep going, do the next right thing, one step at a time. If there is a will, there is a way. Find a way. Make it happen, especially if it's important to you; you can find a way if you identify a challenge.

My teaching approach in school is through positivity and openness. This relaxes the children, and they feel safe to be themselves. They can find solutions when they are happy and content. They find courage.

I need to put my challenges and the learning from that pain to good use. There have been lots of learnings for me. The learning comes from my daily analysis approach, which is similar to journaling. One of the learnings which I'm most proud of is when I decided to lose my fear. To stop accepting that overwhelming fear that I felt about most things.

I was crippled by fear. I was afraid that I would hurt someone, afraid of wasting money, afraid to stand out, afraid to speak my mind, afraid to wear what I wanted, afraid to give an opinion, afraid to be honest, afraid to put my needs first, afraid to admit that I need help, afraid to say that I am not coping.

Once I started to analyse what was affecting my mood each day, I was able to tackle one thing at a time, and that with a combination of open communication, I started to free myself from fear. For example, one time someone commented that I hadn't called to see them for a while. I would generally take that as a criticism and want to explain myself. I would not want to hurt them or offend them with my explanation. Even if it was highlighting that they too have not called to me. Now I have exchanged fear and over-analysis for honesty and communication. So instead, I said, *'I know, but it's nothing personal. I couldn't because I wasn't able to. I have been struggling with my grief, and I just couldn't carry or focus on anything or anyone else. I will be fine, but for now, I need to survive.'*

The second most important learning for me has been having a safety net of small comments to use when needed, encouraging people to think about what they are saying to me. For example, if someone says, *'I suppose you spent a fortune on those shoes, knowing you.'* To that, I would make either one of these replies. I would say, '*really,*' or I would be silent, and when they repeat themselves and ask if I'm listening, I reply, '*I hear you,*' and nothing else. Again, less said is best said.

'I learned long ago, never to wrestle with a pig.
You get dirty, and besides, the pig likes it.'

George Bernard Shaw

Clothes

I love how clothes make me feel. Clothes help me to forget the bad stuff and embrace the good stuff. Clothes make me feel brave, happy, and appreciative.

The colours make me smile. When I find something that works, I'm tickled pink.

They highlight the best bits and camouflage the dodgy bits.

You just can't beat the feeling you get when shopping with friends, from trying on clothes, seeking opinions, looking through your bits when you get home, to dressing up for that simple catch-up or that fab night out.

My body has been through a lot, 10 surgeries, childbirth, cancer, and grief.

There are clothes for every occasion and every mood. Clothes change my mood. I forget about the pains and aches inside my body. They cover the physical pains and aches and mask the emotional ones. They cover the scars, both visible and invisible.

They can keep me grounded, especially when something doesn't work, and elevate me when I receive a compliment from a stranger. I love the banter in the dressing rooms, the support, and the feedback between friends. *'Does my bum look big in this? Do I look wide in this? Am I too short in this?'* and all the positive feedback, *'you look a million dollars, get it in other colours too, I have shoes that would be fab with that dress.'*

I never underestimate the power of clothes. They bring confidence and positivity to my day. Clothes are my armour.

Messages from heaven

Do you believe in messages from heaven? I do. I don't think that I would get this far with my grief if I didn't. Two weeks after my dad's passing, I went to have a spiritual reading. It was booked for me by my friend Finn. When she booked it, my dad was alive, so I was hoping that our friend Brian who had died a few years previous, would come through and guide me at this difficult time. I wasn't prepared for my dad to come through. When I arrived at Theresa's house, she had told me that dad had recently passed. She said that he might not come through because his passing was so recent. As I was walking up her stairs, I heard her say, *'okay, Joe, give me a chance.'* I couldn't believe my ears, but I decided that it was a coincidence and that at the very best, that was my grandad, who had died a few years previous. Unlike my dad, I am not very religious, but I am spiritual and I do have respect for religion, and do I believe that there is something there. After my dad died, I desperately needed to believe that there was an after-life and that there was hope that I would see my dad again someday. There was absolutely no way that I could accept that that was the end, I still can't and won't.

That reading helped me to cross from a place of not coping to a place of hope. I felt that dad was safe. She was amazing. It was mind-blowing what she knew and how she delivered it. She even used his expressions and mannerisms.

Coincidences

Do you believe in coincidences? I completely agree that there are no coincidences in life and that what is for you won't pass you. I will tell you of a lovely story of 'coincidence' and heavenly messages.

I couldn't believe my ears one night as I listened to Niamh Connolly, @transformCBT, on Instagram, read one of my DM's on one of her lives, The ABC's of CBT.

I realised the magic that was unfolding before my eyes. It was breath taking.

The first 'live' that I attended was the third one that Niamh did. I heard her ask about what behaviours we would like to change. Something clicked in me, and I found the urge to type a response. I explained to her that I was entirely new to Instagram. My friends Tara and Kay set it up for me on February 4th, my dad's anniversary and coincidentally, 'World Cancer Day'. They always said that I would love Instagram. They also believed that with all that I have been through between grief, my cancer, my dad's cancer, hearing loss, coeliac disease, retraining to be a teacher, many surgeries, and lifelong illnesses, I might be able to relate with someone and maybe even help someone out there.

Dad died from cancer following his 9-year battle. What a journey I have been on since then. In Niamh's live, I posted the comment, *'I cannot go home since my dad died.'* I live next door to my dad. I couldn't go out to my clothesline after he died because I couldn't face the harsh reality that his silhouette would not be in the window next door. A minute after I posted that, a lady posted, *'I can't go back to my father's grave.'* I cried on the spot and continued to do so for the rest of the 'live'. I knew how she felt. I wanted to so desperately reach out to her, to hug her, to tell her that it will be okay, that she will be okay. But I couldn't. Not because I didn't want to, I certainly wanted to, but because I didn't know how to. I paced the floor up and down, but she wouldn't leave my head or my heart. I also realised the new raw grief that she was experiencing just two weeks after losing her dad. I also realised that I had come through early, terrible raw grief. I had healed a little. I couldn't believe it.

I learned that I had moved on because as I read her message, I remember thinking how I couldn't go back to those early days of grief when it was on top of me. My friend Tara messaged me 'coincidence' to check if I had noticed the lady's message. I told her that I did and how I was devastated for her. Tara told me to message her. I explained that I wanted to but didn't know how to. I didn't know that you could message someone you were not 'following'. Remember, I'm a greenhorn to all of this.

Tara showed me how to message, and I was thrilled. I felt so alive. Then, the doubts set in. I started to question myself. I was afraid that the lady would think I was a lunatic. I didn't know how to reach out when it wasn't a phone call or face-to-face chat. I found those situations simple. I love chatting. But this was new territory for me, and I felt out at sea. Then I remembered what Niamh said on her live I needed to quieten my inner critic. I needed to stick to the facts. I knew that I needed to reach out and do what was right. So I messaged her. A minute later, she messaged back and she was grateful for the message. We chatted until 11.45pm. We had so much in common and we got on like a house on fire.

The following day I sent a message to Niamh to explain the exchange that happened the night before and how she enabled it with the ABC's of CBT. What I didn't know was that the lady had also messaged Niamh to tell of our messages. We have been messaging since, and I gave her my number. We have had lovely conversations, and we both understand each other's pain and suffering, which is very comforting. We have made a connection, and life is all about relationships. Niamh said that we were both messaging her at the same time that she received this poem *A people place by William J.*

Crocker from a friend of hers._Niamh read that poem and I was lost for words.

<u>*A people place*</u>

If this is not a place where tears are understood,
Where do I go to cry?

If this is not a place where my spirits can take wing,
Where do I go to fly?

If this is not a place where my questions can be asked,
Where do I go to seek?

If this is not a place where my feelings can be heard,
Where do I go to speak?

If this is not a place where you'll accept me as I am,
Where can I go to be?

If this is not a place where I can try to learn and grow,
Where can I be just me?

William J. Crocker

It summed up what we were achieving, a place of learning, a place of safety, a place of fun, a place of connection and acceptance. Two days after that live, the lady called me. I was at dad's grave at the time. 'Coincidence?' I don't go that often, and I don't hover at the grave. I just go in and check it over and leave because he is not there. He is everywhere that I go. I don't usually speak at the grave either, but I do make the odd statement, which I did that day. I said as I left the grave. '*Dad, you would have been so proud of me last night reaching out to that lady.*' I am feeling so alive since joining Instagram. I have felt part of a community in a time when I feel so disconnected. I have loved writing my posts, and it's been so refreshing and liberating.

I desperately wanted a sign, a message from heaven that I was on the right track, especially with the posts that I have been putting up. Then, Niamh read that message and that poem. 'Coincidence.' Also, that lady couldn't stay on the live for more than five minutes that night because she had to put her young children to bed. She hated having missed the lives because they were so helpful to her at that time. However, she messaged me after asking if I believed in messages from heaven. I told her to listen to the live, and she would be under no illusion about heavenly messages because our dads have certainly met up in heaven and orchestrated our meeting. I felt so proud of myself for putting up the message, which encouraged her to put up her message, and the rest is history.

On a later conversation, I discovered that her brother works 5 minutes from where I live. He works with one of my best friends' husband. It's such a small world. We are teachers, only daughters, daddy's girls, and both live next to our home houses. I believe and have mentioned it earlier in this book, every challenge in our lives brings beautiful people into our lives to hold our hand and lighten the load.

We are all in this together, and as Niamh said in her live there are more good people than bad people. I believe that we need to reach out, and we also need to take the grip of those who reach out to us. We need to be aware of those around us who might not reach out, and instead, we can try to meet them halfway. Everyone is precious, and everyone has a right to be happy. We are all incredible.

My friend Tara also messaged Niamh, 'coincidence,' and told her that I was like joy on steroids, and it's true. I am getting my mojo back. I am facing my fears. I am starting to share my story and help others while doing it. I am writing, which is something that I had stopped doing. But most importantly, I am investing in myself for the first time in as long as I can remember.

'Letting go of the judgment and the negativity makes space for love and kindness and a passion for everything around you and what you do.'

Holly Willoughby

This chapter is dedicated to Tara, whose Positivity I will cherish forever.

Thoughts provoked from reading this story

Notes:

Story 12: When It's S**t, Say It's S**t

'For to be free is not merely to cast off one's chains, but to live in a way that respects and enhances the freedom of others.'

Nelson Mandela

'The most courageous act is still to think for yourself. Aloud.'

Coco Chanel

Warning! This is where I vent. It's where I have stored all the stuff that I have to fight for and have to deal with.

Did you ever just let out a scream and feel good after it? Did you ever just join in and vent or stand up for yourself because you had enough? I love that advert where the child is having a meltdown in the supermarket and his mother just joins in and throws herself on the ground and has a tantrum. The child stops and looks at her. It is so powerful.

Sometimes, you have to step out of your comfort zone and just call someone out on their behaviour. They might not like it or appreciate it, but if they deserve it, then they will have to deal with it. You can't let people run amuck with your heart or your head.

One thing that I know for sure is that I hate injustice. However, I also strongly feel about paying it forward, thinking about the next person along the path and what you can do to help them. If you have suffered and learned from that suffering, then you should do what's right and help others too. I have both practiced this and benefited from this.

When I went into the radioactive iodine isolation unit, the room was like a little apartment. It had a tiny kitchen, an en-suite, TV, etc. The nuclear medicine guy who checked me in and administered the radioactive medicine, told me that the lady ahead of me paid for the kitchen to be installed to make the weeklong stay in isolation more comfortable for the next person. I was shocked by her generosity but more so by her desire to take what she learned from her week in the unit and to pay it forward by adding what she felt was missing, a kitchen. Bless her. She was, in my opinion, fantastic to do that.

It doesn't have to be a significant act either. I find that when I'm out and about, I see many small ways to help others. Doing random acts of kindness such as holding a door open, giving your unused carpark ticket to the next person or even a smile as you walk past can make someone's day and help them on their way.

My friend Kay is excellent at doing this. The most recent example was when we were going for a walk along the cliff in Ballycotton, we had parked in the nearby carpark. The carpark is on a very severe slope overlooking the cliff. We noticed a lady in the next car crying. Kay went over and asked her if she was ok. She said she was terrified to start her car in fear that it would roll off the cliff. She had a new car and wasn't yet confident about taking off on a slope. With no hesitation, Kay asked her if she would like her to move the vehicle. The lady accepted with great relief. It was a great act to witness. The world needs more of this.

Health is wealth! If you asked me when I was in my twenties if I agreed with the statement 'health is wealth', I would probably have said no. I would probably have said that lots of actual money is wealth. I might extend it to friendships, style, socialising, holidays and work. Good health would have been an entitlement, something that was a given. I was naturally healthy and slim without having to work at it.

My thirties were a turning point for me. I had a lot of challenges to face. Challenges that tested me and challenges that made me. I attribute my coping skills to the solid foundations that I set down when I was a teenager.

Cancer has taken a lot from me, but I'm not going to give without taking. I'm taking something too. I've taken the knowledge that the power of positivity should not be underestimated. I've learned never to take what I have for granted. I try to end each day with a clear conscience and begin each day with hope and spirit in my heart. We can all underestimate our ability to cope with a challenge. We can do amazing things when we put our heart and soul into something.

I feel that having a lifelong illness is like having a part-time job. One must deal with side effects, check-ups, blood tests and scans, consultants, and doctor visits. This all becomes part of your new life. It's work. It takes time, and it costs money. Some appointments can be nerve-racking like facing the leaving cert all over or your driving test. Unfortunately, I don't have a medical card, so I must continue to pay privately for all my appointments.

I love my work. However, I would love to afford to work part-time because this would help me maintain my stamina, especially as I have hypothyroidism, but my medical bills are too high. It's a vicious circle. It's a future goal of mine to work part-time. Dreams and goals are good motivators.

The cost of cancer is real. I have had to take sick leave and days off for appointments. I have run out of paid leave days twice. So I began to plan my operations around what days I had to work back. I remember in 2018 trying to schedule an appointment for endometrial ablation and fallopian tube removal. Unfortunately, I had to wait for the last week in June to have the surgery because I had to work back the days that I lost in the previous years. I could use the summer holidays to recover.

This meant that I had to return to school two days after my surgery. I am not trying to work the system, I am trying to get the system to work for me. I pay for my treatments and surgeries, and it doesn't cost the state a penny. I am not on social welfare. I work very hard, and I pay my taxes.

I sometimes feel that this country is the third world when it comes to health. I am so shocked that the government could find lots of money during a pandemic while people have been suffering in silence for years, on long waitlists.

I was lucky to be able to get health insurance paid for me by my job in Eircom. I struggled to pay this when I was unemployed. We had to cut back on all luxuries to pay for it while I worked to retrain as a teacher.

Another significant expense is the cost of childcare while attending appointments. There is the cost of private consultants, health insurance, drugs, hearing aids, scans, No medical card and no lifelong illness card even though I have a lifelong illness. I will rely on Eltroxin every day for the rest of my life. But it is not on the list, so tough sh**. I should have gotten diabetes, that's on the list. The lifelong illness scheme has not been updated since 1996. It should be called 'the lifelong illness scheme for some, but not all lifelong illnesses.'

I can't get my hearing aids on the medical card because I don't have one. Not that I believe that there are miracles if one had a medical card but I believe it would help a little. It would reduce my monthly prescription to €3 instead of €114. Or €36 per year versus €1,368.

I can't even get a microphone system in my class to hear and teach my pupils effectively. On a positive note, children with hearing loss and impairment can apply for sound systems in their classroom, so that is something.

I am fortunate to have a job. I am now in a situation where I have to continue full-time to pay for my medical bill each year. This pace is ironically contributing to new illnesses. I just want the government to support me like I support the country every week that I pay tax.

Why aren't workers supported for supporting the country? Why can't we get carried for part of the journey? It's almost telling our young that they should get a good education and a good job but pray they don't need the state to support them if they need medical support because they would be better off financially if they quit their jobs if that happens.

I have hypothyroidism. My energy levels are so much lower than they were pre-cancer. To save my life, I have to take from the quality of it. I have to stay under active in terms of my thyroid medication or, as the consultants call it, 'suppressed' so that I don't grow back my thyroid and subsequently my cancer. I find the tiredness so very frustrating.

I don't even want to talk about war wounds, the actual

surgery scars, bowel pacemaker, coeliac, tiredness, lifelong drugs, and lifelong appointments. Another challenge with critical illness is constantly looking over your shoulder - *will I get cancer again?* I feel so angry that I lost my dad after everything that he went through. It might sound strange but as a result of his death, I feel death breathing down my neck as I too had cancer. *Would I be like him? Do my children think that I too will get cancer back and die?* Although from this fear comes the reality that life is short and as a result we should embrace life and live it.

I still get tested. We all do. In March 2020, when I was least expecting it, I was tested again. I was shaken, and I was stirred. Maurice got Covid and grew very ill very quickly. On the night that he was moved to hospital by ambulance, I wrote this and posted it to Instagram. I desperately wanted to protect others from the pain that I was experiencing so profoundly:

I am a teacher working from home.
I am a mother supporting my children's schooling from home.
I am a wife whose husband has Covid.
I am in the high-risk category trying to avoid catching Covid.
I am counting the days, trying to get to the other side.
I am terrified. I have no compass or map and no control.
I thought that cancer was the evil 'C' word, but that has recently extended to Cocooning and Covid.
I am angry. I feel that I've stepped back in time to March 12th, 2020 and that all the hard work and sacrifice of the past year was in vain. But deep down, I know it's not. I know I must stand firm. My love is too deep.
I can't wait until I am up in the early hours because I have been

on a night out and not because I am sitting up worrying about my dearest battling Covid.
He who is my rock is now endangered.
The one who helps me through anything is desperately relying on me for everything.
Energy and vibrancy are replaced with lethargy and fear.
Connection is replaced with distance. So close but yet so far.
Warm embraces are now warm smiles, and kisses are delivered in the air.
Mealtimes are no longer the get-together times. Instead, they are now at a time of separation with meals on trays left outside a closed door.
It feels like he's in another country, but he's only in the next room.

Separation & Sanitisation replaces sitting together and cleaning up together.
Someone of certainty is now your most significant threat.
The sanctuary of that small bubble of hugs and comfort has been taken away.
Watching the same movie on different TVs in different rooms and communicating over the phone and not face to face.
I'd love a cuppa, cake & chat with him as we channel hop on TV.
Check-in for cups of tea by the fire is replaced with temperature and oxygen checks.
My hearing impairment is an even more significant challenge now.

The house that was my sanctuary is now my war zone.
So consumed with helplessness while helping in every way that one can.
It is noting the absence of all that was shared and is now divided.

He was my ears on walks, walks that now have been paused.
Happy nights of chats and hanging out in front of the TV are replaced with ones filled with fear and worry. It is lonely.
The tiredness is aching, but sleep won't come.
The tables have turned, and he is sick.
I'm back in this place of night-time worry and the fear of the unknown.
While we yearn desperately to see our loved ones and to share a warm embrace, it simply is not safe.

It's not fair, challenging, and horrible, but it is the reality.
I am focused and driven by the fact that I'd love to have the opportunity to stay away from my dad to have him alive at the end of all this. But unfortunately, it's easy for me to say that because no distance will bring my dad back from death.
I'd give anything to be 6 feet or six months apart from him and for him not to be 6 feet under.

Our fight must not be misplaced. We must not fight the guidelines, especially now when the end is in sight. Instead, we must focus our fight against this virus - the only way known to succeed, through unity.

Ironically, the disease that causes such physical separation needs emotional inclusion and coming together to beat it.
I'd love to have my hair done. I've fought to bring my hair back from death to cancer, but I understand that it's not the priority at the moment, now my roots symbolise that I'm supporting, I'm following, I'm protecting, and I am keeping safe.
It's lonely, frustrating, and mentally draining but letting it win isn't an option.

Loneliness sets in, and retracing footsteps of sickness past creep up.
Emotions run high while feelings run low.
Watching a loved one suffer has got to be THE most brutal blow.
You are finding the energy to think and plan ahead of a beast that's ripping through your world.

I want to see him drive up the driveway in his van at the end of the working day, and he smiles in the window at me, signalling the lovely evening ahead with kids and dogs in the chorus. 'Dad is home.'
His energy would invade the kitchen, and he would take the towel to the pots and pans and chip in because he is home and support has officially landed.

To have so much support around and to feel so alone.
To have too much time to think and worry and no time for blatant disregard of Covid guidelines.
To get your head in the game with no rules, joy, fairness, and winners.

While most of us follow the guidelines, sadly, others don't get it until they get it.
This isn't a Joke, and we certainly are not laughing.
Six feet apart versus 6 feet under.

Thankfully Maur recovered. I realised yet again how lucky I am.

Now, I am going to stop giving out. Thank you for tolerating that rant. I am stopping because I can hear my dad say, '*Kath, stop. Stop feeding the beast of negativity,*' and he is right. I have said that it can be shit, and I must move on from it or move on with it.

I remember all my dad's sayings, phrases, and analogies. He has said so many to me, and one that I refer a lot to is this, '*you* cannot control the behaviour of others, but you can control how you react to it and cope with it.' He was right because, unfortunately, those behaviours will always exist. They exist to remind of all that is good.

We can compare the bad with the good and hence, appreciate and embrace the good times all the more. These destructive behaviours will always exist so too will your experience with dealing with them. This will give you the strength and ability to rise above them. Try not to let the destructive behaviours take from all the joy that is in your life. Focus on that. Be you. Do you. Stay true to yourself. Put on your coat of armour and move forward.

In the past, I would automatically know my 'go-to' things when I'm feeling low. However, when I was at my lowest when dad died, I would physically have to write down all the positive things in my life and the things, people, and places that lift my spirits because I couldn't think of them automatically. It worked, and now I am back to automatic recalling.

I remember when I was a child, I joined the scouts. I remember the saying 'Bi ullamh.' This means to be prepared or ready. Dad would remind me of this saying. Be prepared for good as well as the bad. Try to be grounded. He was trying to keep me thinking realistically. I was always a dreamer, or as he would put it, 'a Disney princess.'

Similarly, not expecting too much from someone and being realistic will reduce disappointment. I learned, through counselling, that I had very high expectations of people, mainly because I had high expectations of myself. This isn't fair on anyone. I am me, and they are their own person, each of us coming from different backgrounds, upbringings, and circumstances.

My expectations of me are my own and not anybody else's.

I have lowered my expectations of others, and this has led to far less disappointment for me. It has also helped me dig deep into the reasons behind my decisions, looking at my motivations for doing things and establishing if they were pure.

Everything I do is for a reason, and I am not looking for payback or a big reward. It is for that feel-good feeling when you make a friend or loved one happy. It is the most wonderful feeling. I can still have expectations for myself.

There are so many nuggets of advice that come from our parents and grandparents. They have learned them from their experiences of life. I love the Irish sayings and proverbs. Here are some of my favourites;

'An rud is annamh is iontach.'
The rare things in life are best.

'Ní bhíonn an rath acht mar a mbíonn an smacht.'
There is no prosperity without discipline.

'Ní thuigeann an sách an seang.'
You may have to lose a little to understand what it's like to have nothing.

'Ní neart go cur le chéile.'
We are better together. There is strength in unity.

'Níl aon tintéan mar thintéan fhéin.'
There's no place like home.

'Is fear an tslainte na na tainte.'
Health is wealth.

'Is minic a bhris béal duine a shrón.'
A misspoken word will have consequences.

'An té a luíonn le madaí, eiríodh se le dearnaid.'
He who lays down with dogs comes up with fleas —the dangers of mixing with the wrong people.

'Mol an oige agus tiocfaidh sí.'
Encourage young people and they will get there.

Dad was a man of few words, unlike his daughter. He didn't say a whole lot, but you took notice of what he said. He always encouraged me to find the positive in the negative. He warned me not to fuel the fire of hurt by trying to understand why someone has hurt me. Let it go was his advice, rise above it. Do not give it air space because then you are feeding a beast. Instead, he advocated distraction of oneself with the things and people who bring joy. As a result, I learned to create a safe space between myself and negativity.

Dad never burdened anyone with his aches and pains, he was too busy living his life. He was able to compartmentalise. He was respectful of other people's pain too. He lived in the real world. He knew and appreciated that everyone was suffering in their own way and that we are all just trying to do our best with what we have and live our best lives. He reminded me that I had a lot to be thankful for.

The people who warm your soul far outweigh those who try to dim your light. If I came to dad and told him that someone had said something that hurt my feelings, he would say, *'rise above it, Kath, you'd never know what they are going through, give them space, lots of it.'*

Pain will come. It's inevitable. So be prepared, know what heals you, go there. Put on your emotional life jacket and float along for a while until you can swim again. I can hear Dory from the movie, 'Finding Nemo', ringing in my head, just keep swimming, just keep swimming, swimming, swimming. Good times are around the corner.

Because Dad experienced a lot of pain in his life, he began to understand it and learned how to prepare for and shield himself from its extremities. He learned to cope and he taught me. He was inspirational to be around. I loved to be in his company. He oozed this gentle, quiet confidence and became calm in a storm like a strong tree that sways and bends in the storm but doesn't break. He levitated above the problem and spent his time working on a solution or coping mechanism rather than over analysing what had happened. I felt empowered by his example.

He had a vision and a level of patience that was admirable and comparable to few. He had been to the school of life and was happy to share his learnings with whoever was fortunate enough to spend time in his company. I am thankful that my children spent so much time with him. I wasn't finished learning from him, but I will remember and use all that I have learned to survive and thrive as he did. I have so much to draw from, and I'm so lucky to have it all in my head and my heart. For that reason, he will always be alive in me, and his memory will live on. He has paid it forward.

He felt pain, both emotionally and physically, but he never dwelt on it. The odd time he would frown when he was suffering physically and then smile. That's all he had to do for me to feel the total weight of his suffering. I wanted so desperately to take his pain away. But I couldn't. He always asked me to push on and be the best I could be, which gave him incredible energy and strength. He thrived on seeing his children succeed. That was his medicine and his cure and I knew that for sure. That was a priceless thing to behold. He always claimed that he would give us something that money could not buy - strength and strategies to cope — the school of Joe.

He always gave me hope to cope.

Thoughts provoked from reading this story

Notes:

Story 13: Changing what we can.

'Be yourself; everyone else is already taken.'

Oscar Wilde

'Be who you are and say what you feel. Because those who mind don't matter, and those who matter don't mind.'

Bernard M. Maruch

I recently awakened regarding self-care, and I wanted to share it because it might help you too. I love to find new strategies to make life better. It's even better again still if I can share and help somebody else.

I have been frustrated by my hectic lifestyle for a long time. I know that I am a busy person, and I like to be engaged. However, there is being active, and there is being hectic. If you want to get something done, ask a busy person, so I tend to get asked to do a lot. When you are taking care of everyone, who is taking care of you? As a result, I don't seem to have any time for self-care. I became envious of people making time for self-care.

I wondered how they achieved it. It's challenging to find

the time when you are juggling everyday life. I know that this is something that I can and should change.

My life was probably at its busiest about four years ago. My Dad was dying, I was heartbroken, juggling my full-time job, poor health, family, running dad's company, managing his estate, dad losing his cancer battle and the grief that followed, and I was burnt out. So I have to ask myself, *what's my excuse now?*

I realised that every year of our lives is a busy year. We keep putting something on where we take something else off. *Is it as simple as prioritisation?* I wonder.

I listened to a Ted Talk recently about self-care by Susannah Joy Winters. She said that there is a myth that self-care was about spa days, pedicures, and Prosecco. It is not. These things are lovely, but they don't restore us. She asked the question: *what is self-care, and how can we practice it?* Selfcare is deliberately taking care of our wellbeing through restorative acts. One of the greatest threats to our wellbeing is physical and emotional stress, what we put in our bodies, on our bodies and our thoughts. She got me thinking. *What do I do for self-care? What can I change?*

I love clothes, and dressing up has always helped me forget my sadness, relieve my anxieties and mask my scars. This brings me joy, but it's not self-care. I don't do anything for self-care. *Why? What are the barriers for me? Is it mothers' guilt, working mothers' guilt?, lack of time?, expectations?, procrastination?, judgment? Or Prioritisation? What is it? Am I afraid of what I'll hear myself think if I was silent?*

This makes me feel overwhelmed because I know I need to invest in self-care, but what do I take off my list to put self-care on? I made it my mission that I would become aware of what I was doing with my time for one week. I went on a fact-finding mission to help me establish what I could change in my life. When I arrived at my daughter's school 15 minutes before collection time to get parking, I noticed that I could close my eyes and sleep for those 15 minutes instead of checking emails, making calls, or scrolling on my phone. It was bliss.

I began to realise that it's about making healthier choices about the time you have, however little of it you have. I also noticed that I am brilliant at writing to-do lists for work but useless at writing them for my personal Life. I now sit at night for 5 minutes before turning on the TV and writing a list of things that I want to achieve the next day. I went a step further and put my list into categories:

1. What I must do.
2. What I'd like to do.
3. What I'd love to get done.

This helps me reassure myself that I am in control, that tomorrow is another day, it is achievable. I can see it on a list. I was at war with myself. Forcing myself to get it all done, and if I didn't, I would beat myself up about it. I would ask myself if I am not lazy, why can't I achieve it all?

I realised that I spend most of my day meeting the needs of others. I am also spending too much time cleaning and organising my home, almost punishing myself for having a full-time job, one that I need. I had fallen victim to being busy almost for the sake of it. I needed to admit and accept that. I needed to change that.

I am very hard on myself. I work full time, am a mum to two, a wife, and a friend. I have a lifelong illness that affects my energy *levels, and I am only human. It's only when I say this to myself out loud that I realise that I wouldn't speak to a friend the way I speak to myself.*

When I see what I achieve in a day, I am more aware of all that I accomplish. I strongly recommend this exercise. I can be my own worst enemy. They say that gratitude is the antidote to anxiety and stress. I am trying to tell myself and remind myself of all the things that I am grateful for. I am changing how I speak to myself and how I care for myself.

The major obstacle for me was that I was in denial as to what to do for self-care. I was clueless. I am so aware that every time I go for a hospital check-up, they remind me to make a better effort with my self-care and slow down my pace. I make a significant effort with my house, job, family, friends, and image but neglect my inner self. She is exhausted and crying out for help. I need to stop and just do it.

It's about showing up for yourself every single day. Just to imagine, *what would be possible if we did that?* By making wellbeing an essential part of our lives. This is something that was emphasised and highlighted more during the pandemic.

This is precisely what Susannah Joy Winters was getting at in her Ted talk — stepping away from denial. Instead, she encourages three therapeutic activities each day:

<u>Three Daily Therapeutic Activities</u>

1. **Moments of stillness in silence.** This can be just sitting comfortably in your chair, car, bath, meditation if you can, if not just sitting with yourself. Calming the outside and inside noises. This will bring awareness to those thoughts, and with understanding, we can adjust what we keep and what we lose.

2. **Increase movement.** Even just 10 minutes a day can have a considerable impact.
3. **Time in nature.** Get outside!

Sleep is crucial. Everything looks better after a good night's sleep. Sleep is usually the first thing that goes for me when I am stressed. I can go to sleep no problem, but I will wake after a couple of hours, and falling back to sleep after waking is a considerable challenge. I start to think, and I run to-do lists in my mind. I scroll on my phone, and I begin to miss my dad. I cry, then I get up and do something to distract myself. I became busy again. I now accept that this is the opposite of what I actually should do.

It's about small actionable steps. I listened to a podcast recently by Arianna Huffington. She spoke about micro-steps. Actions that are too small to fail. - I think that is brilliant. Simplify the step to what you can achieve.

If your action or goal is to remove your phone from your bedroom so that you don't go on it when you wake, then try to remove it for the week, if this is not achievable, then try one night per week, if this is not achievable then move it away from your nightstand to the other side of your bedroom — micro-steps.

She also mentions a daily ritual of taking 60 seconds for yourself before you do anything so that you get to set your intention for the day. To reconnect with yourself before the world comes at you. It is being present with yourself. In that 60 seconds, you are reminding yourself of all that you are grateful for.

I did a self-care course with the fabulous Dr. Clodagh at @thewellnesspsychologist on Instagram. This was an excellent investment for me because there was accountability. She encourages taking time out and meditation, starting with one minute of meditation then slowly adding another minute.

She has set a challenge of doing one thing you need to do and one thing you love to do. For example, I **need** to book an eye test. I'd **love** to have a long bath. She encourages us to do 5 minutes of self-care reflection in a diary or notebook.

If our goals didn't work out, consider the 'why' instead of putting energy into being hard on yourself. Then, reflect on how you could do things differently to help achieve self-care goals next time. Maybe simplify the plan as Arianna Huffington advises with her micro-steps. In summary, it's not about big plans and spending lots of time or lots of money. It's free. It's about stopping for short periods and doing absolutely nothing.

I recently saw a TikTok video by @iamqueenskye; she reminded us of what Buddha said regarding the biggest mistake in Life: We think we have time;

'Time is free, but it is priceless. You cannot own it, but you can use it. You can't keep it, but you can spend it, and once it's gone, you can never get it back.' I found these words very grounding and truthful.

All of this has helped me to achieve self-care because it has explained to me what self-care is, it has given me strategies, made me analyse my time, made me think about what excuses I make to myself, I discovered how I waste time and as a result made self-care achievable for me. I have changed what I can change. I hope that it helps you too.

'Look after your physical, emotional, mental, and spiritual health and wellbeing. If you don't value yourself, nobody else will.'

Anne Devine, Encourage yourself, encourage others

Thoughts provoked from reading this story

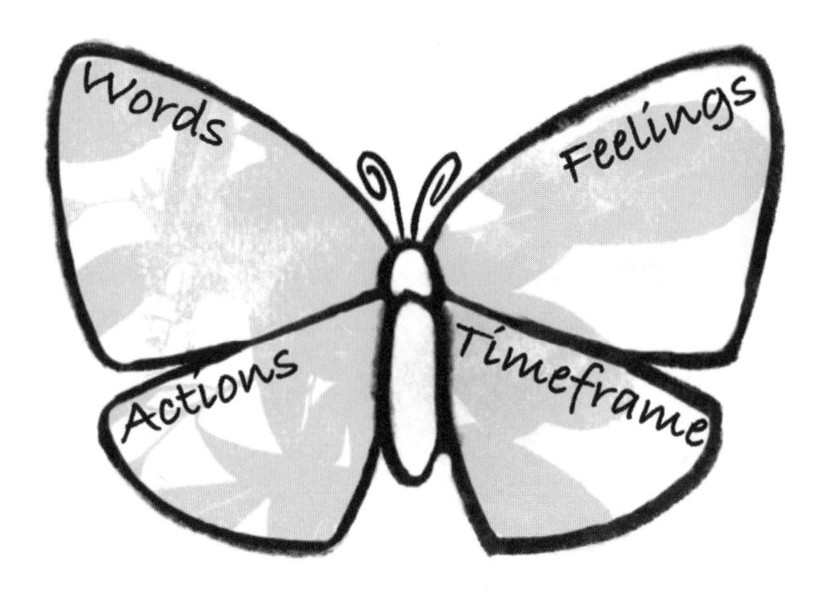

Notes:

Story 14: Working Woman

'Be a strong woman so your daughter will have a role model, and your son will know what to look for in a woman when he's a man.'

Motivational quotes for women

'There is no force more powerful than a woman determined to rise.'

Bosa Sebele

In the early 1970s, my father was transferred to Cork from the Department of Agriculture. He took digs with a lovely lady. In that time all young men were spoiled by their landladies. My dad was of course ruined. His landlady being so warm and loving, was the perfect landlady for dad. He loved her. In his evenings off work, dad would drive around looking out for a plot of land to buy to build a house. He had no fear when it came to achieving his goals. His lack of fear stood to him time and time again. If he wanted something, he found a way to get it. As well as having no fear, he was quietly confident in himself. He had no insecurities about asking for what he needed and wanted.

On one of his evening drives, he spotted a site for sale. He inquired about it, but discovered that it was out of his budget. He wanted it and knew that he had to find a way to get it. He applied for a part-time job in a nearby pig farm. He worked most evenings and saved the money he earned. Then, he went back to the bank, and they approved his loan for the site. He knew that he couldn't afford to build on the site for some time and he decided to buy a welder. This enabled him to earn more money part-time and resulted in him getting his mortgage approved.

Years later, we asked dad why there was a sink in every bedroom in our house. He told us that when he applied for his mortgage, he thought he might have to rent out a room or two to help with the mortgage payments. Having a sink in every room gave him the safety of being ready to rent if he needed to.

Our mother was a brilliant nurse but gave up her job to raise a family. Dad was the sole earner in our home. Dad's entrepreneurial skills didn't settle there. He converted the garage at home to an engineering shed and used one of the bedrooms at the bottom of the hall as an office. I loved the office. I am sure that I annoyed the secretary daily. I lived down there. I sat and wrote notes, coloured, copied what they wrote, and was first at the door when dad was going out to price a job or pay a bill.

He went on to employ some men, and his business grew. He diversified from engineering work into building houses. I loved to be in his company. From an early age, I knew that you had to work hard for what you want. I knew that you have to grab opportunities with both hands and stay focused on your goals if you wanted to reach them. If there was a will, there was a way. If we ever wanted anything that wasn't a necessity, we would have to convince my dad because there was no way that he was going to have spoiled children.

We learned the art of sales at a very early age. I remember wanting a Labrador pup. I asked dad, and he said no. He claimed that no one would mind him and he would be 'landed' with him. I knew that I would have to prove him wrong. So I collected every dog advert from every Cork Examiner newspaper for weeks and then covered the back of his bedroom door with them. Every time I earned money, I told him that I was keeping it for the price of the dog. He eventually caved in, and I got Kim. I loved him and cared for him for 14 years until he died. Dad loved him too.

My first job was at a local hair salon when I was 13 years old. I spent my Saturdays sweeping up and washing hair. I got £10. This was gold to me. I couldn't get to Cork quickly enough to spend it. I always loved to shop, and I loved all things girly. Whenever I would go to Cork with my friends shopping, Dad gave me my bus and lunch money. I earned this during the week making dinner every day and doing housework and homework with my younger brothers. Dad ensured that we had a good firm grip on reality.

When I went to college, I always had a part-time job and a summer job. I had the best summer job working for Irish Distillers at their Heritage centre. When I graduated from college, I continued to work at the heritage centre until it closed at the end of the season in November. This meant I had to get my first real full-time job.

I found it challenging to get a job. I registered with recruitment agencies, and they kept reminding me that I had no experience, so I couldn't secure a job. I knew I could be an excellent employee, but I just couldn't break into any company.

I enrolled in a marketing course because they offered a work placement to the person with the best end-of-course results. I worked my backside off on that course, and I was placed with a software company. I hated it. My dad reminded me that I would not always like what I do while on the way up the ladder, but I must climb respectfully and gracefully. Shortly after, I applied for the graduate programme with the Bank of Ireland. I worked there for two years, during which time I applied for and got my mortgage approval.

I went on to join Eircom as a sales representative. I smashed my targets and made some great friends. As soon as I got the chance, I applied for a promotion. It was a team leader position, my big chance to prove my leadership qualities. The only problem was that I had no leadership experience except for my 'boss role' at home. I went into the interview and told them about all the little strategies and approaches that I used at home and how I juggled it all and made it work. I got the job, and I was off.

I worked hard and moved up through the company to become regional Sales Manager for Key Accounts. I worked with a team of 8 Key account managers, and we covered the area of Munster and Leinster. It was a fast-paced, glamorous job, and I loved it. I loved the sales calls and problem solving, I adored writing the presentations and training courses.

Following the birth of my daughter, my past crept up and bit me. I couldn't bear to be away from her. This job was amazing and presented me with substantial future opportunities but I was deeply lonely for Mia, and I knew that I wanted to be involved in my children's lives, not just passing in and out. It wasn't for me.

I knew that I wanted to work and have a career, but at a more manageable pace and quality of life that allowed me to be a hands-on mother. Six months after returning from maternity leave, I handed in my notice and left that life behind me when Mia turned one.

The next leg in my career was the most challenging one. I enrolled to study the Leaving Cert Irish paper as a mature student. Mia was three, and Colin was four months old. They say that what doesn't break you makes you stronger. I'm still not sure about that one. I still have the war wounds. I have no regrets, but I'm glad that I didn't know what I was getting myself into. Ignorance is bliss in this case.

I sat my Leaving Cert the month after Colin's first birthday and went on to apply to Hibernia College to study for my teaching diploma. In the meantime, Colin had developed rubella and night terrors, so all the money that I saved while in Eircom went on supporting him. I had to get a loan for my course. The bank would only give me a loan if my dad went to guarantee for me, which he did.

I'm so grateful to the universe for pushing me to follow my heart and change careers to work better with my changing personal life. As a result, I was always there for my children. I started school the same day as Mia. I was always there for my dad too. If I'd have stayed with Eircom, I would have probably ended up relocating to Dublin and setting up my life there to accommodate my job. That would have been lovely too, but I wouldn't have been able to be there for my dad. And that's something that I would have regretted. There is a lot to be said for going with your heart and with your gut instinct.

Fear can choke a lot of plans. I had fear back then. Of course I did. I was leaving a fabulous job to become unemployed, to become a mature student and full-time mum. It was extra pressure on my husband to make ends meet financially. I had to face setting up a new career path. But I will say that a one step at a time approach certainly helped. This was an occasion whereby looking at the big picture would have led to procrastination for me, I am sure.

Even as I write this book, I can feel the fear creep in. It's genuine and very normal to be afraid of change and to be scared of messing up. I roll questions in my head all the time. Questions such as, *what if my book doesn't sell? What if I end up with a vast publishing and printing bill? What if people laugh at me and ask,* what was she thinking of, writing a book about her experiences'? But I must also think that maybe just one other person is out there today who might read my book and get a little something from it and take the plunge to do something they want to do but are afraid of. Or someone who might just need to identify with someone else's shit and feel that they are not alone in their shit.

Failing is a real thing, but I know that I'm not trying to hurt anyone or live anyone else's life. I am trying to live my best life. Yes, it could fall on its face. But it could be a great thing too. I will never know unless I try. There is one thing that I have most certainly learned from facing death head-on, I will have no regrets. Better to have tried and failed than to have never tried at all. This is a saying that I strongly agree with.

When I weigh up the pros and cons, I believe that as a mother and role model to my children, I would undoubtedly prefer not just to tell them but show them that they must follow their dreams, put themselves out there and go for what they feel honest about.

Everyone knows that one thing that makes them feel alive, so why not do more of it or do it for as much of your life as you possibly can. So what if you try something and it fails? You can always try something else and move on again. You can take learnings away and make adjustments based on those learnings.

You are here to live your life for yourself, not a life that suits other people or looks acceptable to other people. When my dad faced death, he was incredibly proud of his life. He especially mentioned his first failed company and said he had no regrets. It worked very well for a long time and employed a lot of people. It made him very happy, and he would have hated to die wondering what if. He also said that when his building company failed, it taught him valuable lessons that would result in his next company being very successful.

Mistakes and failures are how we learn, and they should not be catalysts for quitting or giving up on our dreams. Whenever I think about the what if's, and's or buts, I ask myself one very straightforward question. Would I prefer not to write and be safe with hidden dreams or write and fulfil my most cherished life goal?

It's amazing what doors open when the universe supports you following your dreams. I am writing this to give back. I am fundraising for cancer research to give cancer the two fingers by helping to make more survivors. I am trying to fight back against a disease that took my dad away from us. But also, I am the best that I can be for myself. Isn't that what any parent wants for their loved ones, to be the best they can be for themselves. I know that's certainly what my dad wanted.

There will be challenges along the way, and the fight is good for us, it makes the win all the more pleasurable. One step at a time, you can do anything that you want to do. Let's face it, you will be interested in what your dream thing is, which will help you go a very long way. You will find a way if it's something that you love to do.

Sometimes it helps to do a worst-case scenario analysis. *So in the context of this book, let's just say that I lose confidence and don't put it out there, then what?* Well, it will be a little life story for my children to read and pass on. I would love it if I had one from my dad. I can still fundraise for cancer research in another way, and I would have been seen to have tried in the eyes of my children. *Who cares anyway?* If it matters to you, then it matters.

Fundraising through writing is my way of giving all of me to the cause, the good, the bad, and the ugly. I noticed that one would get little messages of support along the way, which will carry you along. For example, I remember writing a piece about Covid when Maurice was very unwell with it. I posted it on Instagram. So many people told me that they had let down their guard and that my piece had encouraged them to re-focus and put back up their guard and stay safe. That was a profound message of support to me about my writing.

I put up another piece about grief, and the number of people who called me to say how much it helped them was overwhelming. It made me realise that I could now accept that I have a way with words, this was my thing. It was the thing that had always been there throughout my life, hovering below the surface. Maybe there would be no book, but there will always be those two pieces that helped someone, and that felt amazing. My dad would be proud. I am pleased, but most importantly, I am doing what I love.

Maybe it's about talking a bit of sense into yourself. I watched the Friend's Reunion show with my daughter last week. She is a big Friends fan. I am too. She told me that she watched some interviews with the cast. She told me how Joey's, actor Matt le Blanc's mum was nervous about him being an actor. She asked him what he knew about acting. But he had a gut feeling, a passion for it. He knew that he had to do it to quieten the voice in his head. So the interviewer asked Matt what his mother would say now, to which he replied *'thank you for the Mercedes.'*

Thomas Edison said, when trying to invent the lightbulb, *'I have not failed, I have just found a thousand ways how not to do it.'* I sound like I'm preaching now, so I will end this rant with what I hope will be a thought-provoking question. *What's on your bucket list?*

> *'Bring your talent into the open. Embrace it and celebrate it. Share it with others.'*

Anne Devine, Encourage yourself, encourage others.

Thoughts provoked from reading this story

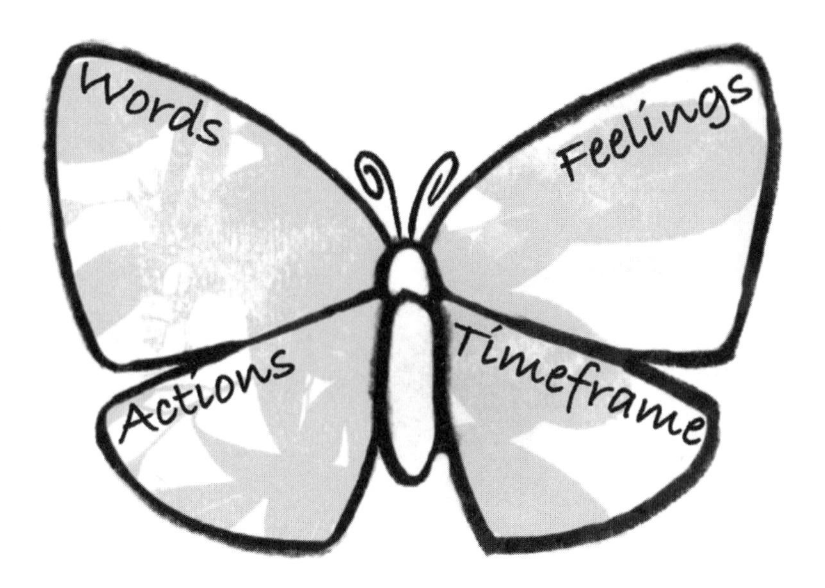

Notes:

Story 15: Happiness

'Happiness is a state of mind. It's just in accordance to how you look at things.'

Walt Disney

We are all in pursuit of happiness. We would also probably agree that joy has taken on a new meaning since the Covid 19 Pandemic. We are finding happiness again in the simple things, and we are realising that happiness comes from within first.

For this story, I asked my school children to help me. I asked them the question. *What is happiness?* At first, they threw out sentences such as '*when you laugh or smile, you know you are happy.*' Then, they thought a little more deeply and said, '*When you feel warm and 'jumpy' inside, like you are walking on a cloud.*' We looked up the word 'happiness' in the dictionary, and we found the following definition:

'Happiness is that feeling that comes over you when you know life is good, and you can't help but smile. It's the opposite of sadness. Happiness is a sense of well-being, joy, or contentment. When people are successful, safe, or lucky, they feel happiness. No one ever complained about feeling too much happiness.'

I asked the children to chat amongst themselves and brainstorm the word 'happiness.' We got back together as a whole class. I wrote the word happiness in a heart on the board. The children called out comments to describe happiness. *Home, friends, holidays, kind words, play dates, pizza, PlayStation 5, art, the beach etc.* The one common denominator was that each involved spending time with loved ones.

I asked them if they could tell if someone was happy. The children said they could because if someone were happy, they would have a smile. I asked them how happiness feels. They said 'warm.' We decided to write categories on the board - people, places, experiences, words, and actions. We then thought about happiness in the context of these headings. Children embrace the simple things in life. They can teach us a thing or two about happiness and gratitude. I encouraged them to think laterally about happiness and about how to achieve satisfaction.

Quite a few of them said that happiness could be blocked by 'bullies.' I reminded them that the 'bully' is devoid of joy, and because of this, they lash out at others to make them unhappy. Of course, we must not hurt the 'bullies,' but we must ignore their hurtful behaviour. I explained that it's not the person who is wrong, it is the behaviour. I encouraged them constantly to try to be kind. To factor in the fact that sometimes people can have a bad day and take it out on the wrong person.

I went on to explain that we can't be happy all of the time. There are lots of emotions, and they all have a place in life. That is life. Only when we experience feelings of sadness and anger can we truly celebrate and appreciate happiness and love. I compared it to Christmas day. We would soon tire of it if it were Christmas day every day, although they disagreed with me.

I asked them to think about ways to spot a person who was unhappy or having a bad day and to think about how they could help improve someone's bad day. This was a great lesson in understanding and appreciation. They also learned how to better communicate with each other if they have a bad day and ask for help or support. They also learned about the various ways to reach out and help others feel happy. For example, by doing random acts of kindness such as helping others with their work, inviting others to join in a game, sharing, or just a simple smile, every child could raise another child's spirits and even make their day.

I compiled their feedback and arranged it into six categories - people, places, actions, words, things, and experiences. I was taken aback by the fact that there were not many material things listed. Instead they spoke about friends, family, nice things that people said to them and times when they had happy experiences with friends and loved ones. It got me thinking about what happiness was like at different stages of our lives. *What was happiness to you when you were a young child versus now?* For me, happiness has always been there. I'm naturally a happy-go-lucky person, and I tend to have a smile on my face most of the time. When I was a girl, people would call me 'a pleasant little thing.' Both my parents and grandparents have the same warm, happy look about them, and I notice it in my children, brothers, aunts, uncles, nieces and nephews. Happiness to me as a child were those long summer days filled with fun, freedom and exploration.

I learned as I got older that you don't get happiness from someone or something. You get joy from yourself, from within. We all look to other people and want their satisfaction. That is like a game of cat and mouse, and the cat is always chasing. Comparing yourself to others can lead to despair. Don't look to others. Try to look within yourself. Ask yourself what makes you happy and surround yourself with that. Start from the seed of being happy within instead of looking outwards; otherwise, you will be constantly bombarded by the happiness of others.

If you are unhappy with yourself, work on pairing back what happened to you and accepting it. Get help and support if you need it. Your happiness is paramount too. Learn that happiness doesn't just happen; you have to work at it. I read a fantastic analogy recently on the Instagram page of ehopkins, therapy coach, and I loved it:

'You are holding a cup of coffee when someone comes along and bumps into you or shakes your arm, making you spill your coffee everywhere.

Why did you spill your coffee?
Because someone bumped into me!

Wrong answer.
You spilled your coffee because there was coffee in your cup.
Had there been tea in the cup, you would have spilled tea.
whatever is inside the cup will spill out
Therefore, when life comes along and shakes you (which will happen) whatever is inside you will come out. It's easy to fake it until you get rattled.
so we have to ask ourselves... what's in my cup?
When life gets tough, what spills over?
Joy, gratefulness, peace, and humility?
Anger, bitterness, harsh words, and reactions?
Life provides the cup. YOU choose how to fill it.'

That's something to think about for sure. *What is blocking our happiness? What are we carrying in our hearts every day? What is in our cups? Can we fill our cup with peace and happiness?*

Another one to think about is the analogy of a 'white page with the black dot' - concentrate on the black dot as unhappiness, a minimal space on the page, look at the white page, happiness. There are a lot more happy things and happy times in life. Seek them out and enjoy them. You are entitled to happiness.

Happiness is closely linked to how we think and feel about the world and how we perceive our experiences. Are we judging from a happy place or a sad place? I believe that we can build happiness from gratitude for all the good that we each have in our lives. Specific actions or habits, such as regular exercise, eating healthily, meditating, connecting with other people, savouring the good times, making memories, and even regularly smiling and laughing, make us happy.

Laughter has always been like medicine to me. Laughing relaxes me and makes me happy deep within myself. Character traits such as self-control, fairness, caring about others, courage, leadership, and honesty build up happiness too. You can't beat the feeling that you get from helping someone and them being grateful for it. It is lovely to be able to put a smile on someone's face. We can each can do that.

We must teach children constructive mental habits that create happiness. Habits such as managing our moods, teaching and practicing positive self-talk, nurturing optimism show them that life is worth celebrating. Get excited. Show them that you get excited too and talk about how wonderful that feeling is. Children love when adults act silly. Their little faces light up, so be silly and have fun.

We are role models for our children, and they copy and feed

off what they see and what they are exposed to. Practicing gratitude and appreciating our connectedness to each other and the entire universe are all habits that make us happier. Build these into your life together, so you model them regularly and talk about using them. Over time, your child will follow your lead.

A simple daily attitude of gratitude check-in can be very beneficial. List the things that you are grateful for each day. For example, when I collect my children from school, I ask them to tell me one good thing about their day. I find that they are quick to point out all the bad stuff, but focusing on one good thing can give them perspective. Tell them that you love and respect them. Listen to them and tell them that you understand them. Tell them that you are proud of them.

Self-management routines that create happiness like regular exercise, eating healthy, yoga and meditation are linked to happiness levels. I mentioned in my previous story about making time for self-care. It can be as simple as catching a 15 minute walk near the school as you are waiting for your children. Some people love music, and it is an immediate mood lifter for them; for others, a walk, yoga, or a run works best.

Remember in Story 7 when we spoke about being your cheerleader? We all need a cheerleader to help us over life's many hurdles. *Who says we can't be our own? In fact, who better?* Give yourself reassurance, acknowledgment, praise, and pep talks. Talk to yourself like someone you love aloud so your kids can hear you.

Make sure your response to failure is, *'I just haven't figured this out YET,'* or *'I just haven't practiced this enough YET.'*

Practicing optimism can protect us against unhappiness. Some of us are indeed born more optimistic than others, it's challenging to be hopeful sometimes, but we can all try to cultivate it. We can become happier by noticing the simple things in life. Point out the simple something to your children. Talk to them. We are ever more aware of this since the pandemic. Children learn by our example what's essential in life. As Albert Einstein said, *'There are only two ways to live your life. One is as though nothing is a miracle. The other is as though everything is a miracle.'*

The old saying that laughter is the best medicine turns out to be true. The more we laugh, the happier we are! This is because it changes our body chemistry.

It's essential to prioritise relationships. Relationships take work but they're worth it. We are all learning about each other every day.

'We tend to forget that happiness doesn't come as a result of getting something we don't have, but rather of recognising and appreciating what we do have.'

Frederick Keonig

Many people think they can't be grateful until they are happy, meaning they have something to be thankful for. But look closely, and you'll find that it's the opposite, people are happy because they are grateful. People who describe themselves as consciously cultivating gratefulness are happier.

Children don't have a context for life, so they don't know whether they are lucky or unlucky, only their friend Johnny has more expensive trainers. But there are many ways to help children learn to cultivate gratitude instead of taking everything for granted.

First, continue to model this for them. Say things like, *'I am lucky that I have a lovely home, I am lucky to have a family who loves me, I am lucky to have a job and good friends.'*

I mentioned the Disney movie 'Inside out' in Story 3. This was a fantastic movie which explained the various emotions to children. Accept all emotions. Life is full of joy, but life is also full of loss and pain, and there are reasons to grieve, even for the happiest person. Acknowledging our sad feelings isn't focusing on the negative. Instead, it's opening ourselves to the full range of being human. Accepting those uncomfortable, painful feelings deepens our ability to take joy into our lives.

Choosing to be happy doesn't mean repressing our feelings. It means acknowledging and honouring all our emotions and letting ourselves feel them. You cannot help how you feel. Expressing our feelings allows us to move through the emotions, so they start to dissolve. When my dad died, I tried to hide in my bedroom when I needed to cry and dispel my grief, but my children could tell that I was very sad from my red eyes. I could see the worry appear on their faces. I decided to allow them to see my feelings, and I started to cry in front of them. I explained that I was very sad and lonely for Granddad, and they would hug and support me. They learned how to help another person in sadness. That is a valuable lesson.

I explained that it was ok to cry because my tears were the measure of my love. It is essential to show your child that it is ok to feel upset and to empathise with your child's upset feelings because this will allow her to handle them and help the feelings start to evaporate so she can move on. This is not a process that can be rushed, so give your child and yourself whatever time you need.

Most people don't know that they can let bad moods go and consciously change their perspectives. Practice in doing this can make us happier. You can practice this by monitoring your moods, allowing yourself to feel the emotions while you hold yourself with love, noticing any negative thoughts that give rise to the feelings. Remember the 'Daily analysis' that I spoke about in a chapters 3 and 11. This will help you to find out what is feeding your emotions and feelings.

Once you know what is affecting your mood, you will then choose a thought or an action that makes you feel a little better. The hard part is changing a bad mood while you're in it. Just find a way to help yourself feel slightly better. That allows you to face what's upsetting you and try to solve it. Sometimes just changing the way we're thinking about a situation shifts things. Sometimes writing it down can take it out of our heads.

As parents, we need to remember that we are not the only ones teaching our children about life. They get the constant media message that the goal of life is more money and more things. Ultimately, what we model and tell them will matter more, but we need to confront those destructive messages directly. I believe that communication is vital. We must find time to communicate with our children.

I believe that it is vital to find ways for children to make a positive difference in the world to enjoy and learn from this experience. We can model helping out. We can model being kind. We can model coping.

'What do you want to be when you grow up?'
'Kind,' said the boy.

Charlie Mackesy. The boy, the mole, the fox, and the horse.

*'They asked her; What is real happiness?
She answered; Happiness is not fulfilling every
pleasure or getting every outcome you desire.
Happiness is being able to enjoy life with a
peaceful mind that is not constantly craving
for more. It is the inner peace that comes with
embracing change.'*

Yung Pueblo

Thoughts provoked from reading this story

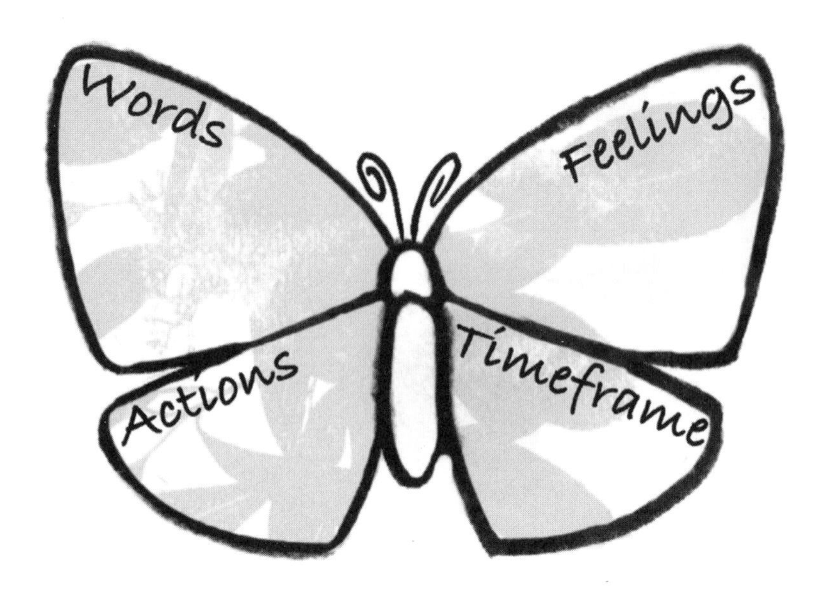

Notes:

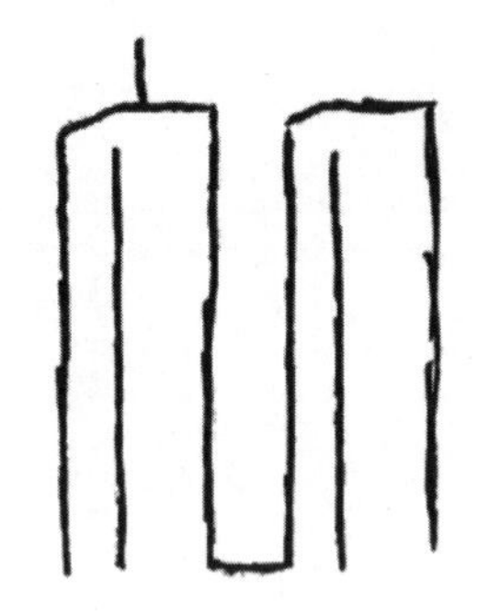

Story 16: Sweet 16 - To Have And To Hold

'We can only learn to love by loving.'

- Rumi

'All of me loves all of you.'

- John Legend

'Never doubt that I love.'

- William Shakespeare

I have saved the best until last. The story of how I met the love of my life, Maur, Maurice Griffin Junior.

Shakespeare has always been associated with love – his classic plays and poems throughout the centuries are widely studied and enjoyed and still poignant today. When I contemplate writing about love, Shakespeare immediately comes to mind. Everyone has a love story to tell, and this is mine.

I attended Cloyne National School in the early 1980s. It was a small country school strongly supported by the community.

We lived a mile from the school, so our mother dropped us off every day and collected us afterwards. Life was straightforward back then. You went to school, came home, did your homework, and went outside and played until it was dinner time. At half-past eight, whether it was bright or dark, you went to bed. I couldn't wait to start school. I drove my parents crazy every day, begging them to allow me to start school.

Back then, if the school were at risk of losing a teacher, they would reach out to the community to see if any child was nearly ready for school and that child got brought in early. I was one of those children, and I was more than happy to oblige. When I started school in junior infants, or as we called it, baby infants, my husband, Maurice, was in senior infants, or big infants, so we were in the same classroom.

When I think back to my days in primary school, they make me smile. I loved school. My brothers hated school. I loved it so much that I would come home and play school on my blackboard in the garage. Little did I know that I was sitting and playing a few meters away from my future husband.

The years went by, and Maur and I crossed paths again on a Christmas trip home from college at nineteen years of age. My eldest brother told me that Maur 'fancied me'. My romantic thoughts of marriage and happily ever after were bruised by the ideas of my parents' failed marriage. As a result, I had decided that I wasn't ever going to marry. Instead, I would throw myself into my work and my career.

However, the universe had other plans for me. On New Year's Eve 1994, we shared our first kiss. I loved him instantly, and I knew that I always would. It was more love at first chat and kiss rather than first sight despite him being very handsome. I had practically known him all my life. However, I was in college in England, he worked in Ireland, so we went our separate ways. That was until a week later when I received my first letter from Maur. We continued to write, then he would call me. That time it was phone boxes and landlines, no mobiles. The phone bills increased, and the connection grew.

While on Easter break from college, March 9th, 1995, Maur asked me to go steady. We were inseparable. We spoke on the phone every day, we wrote to each other and every time I could, I came home. When I did come home, I lived in his ear. While he was building his rally car, I would sit in it studying. I loved being in his company. I still do today. I loved the simple spins in the car, van, or lorry, whatever he was driving and wherever he was going, I was happy to be going there too.

Time went by, and I graduated from college and returned to live at home. Then, on New Year's Eve 1998, we got engaged. I was working for the bank at the time, and Maur had just qualified as a mechanic. We built our own home in 2000 and got married on September 14, 2001. This day is also known as the national day of mourning following the events of 9/11, a week I will remember forever, and so will everyone else.

On 9/11, I left a meeting at work and walked to the Jewellers to collect our wedding rings. I had my phone turned off all morning during my appointments and hadn't turned it back on by the time I reached the jewellers. I had spent my time reading my lovely wedding card that I received from my sales team as I walked, when I went to the counter, a crowd of people has huddled around. A lady approached me and asked if she could help me. I explained that I was collecting our rings and gave my name. She left momentarily and returned with the two little boxes. But, again, I was in my wedding bubble, totally unaware of what was unfolding in New York.

It had been a busy few months and a crazy last week of organising everything at work so that I could take two weeks off, not to mention the business that comes with managing a wedding. The shop assistant commented on the engravings on our wedding rings 'only you' and asked when we were getting married, and I replied '*this Friday,*' she then asked where we were going on honeymoon. I excitedly told her, '*New York.*' Her face changed. She commented, '*God, wasn't it awful what happened there this morning.*' I hadn't a clue what she was talking about. She could tell from my face. She guided me to a small room out the back. She was so lovely.

You always remember the kind person when something terrible happens to you. I could not believe my eyes or ears. I stepped outside, and I called Maur. He confirmed what had been happening in New York.

The September 11 attacks, often called 9/11, were a series of four coordinated terrorist attacks by the Wahhabi Islamist terrorist group Al-Qaeda against the United States on the morning of Tuesday, September 11, 2001. I think that anyone who remembers that day will say it was a surreal experience to watch. The devastation was overwhelming. Everyone remembers where they were that day. We pretty much spent the rest of that day watching the coverage of the events of 9/11. It was the most horrific thing I ever did see. I cried all day.

'*No day shall erase you from the memory of time.*' This is written on the wall at the 911 Memorial and Museum in New York City.

'It's also a memory of bravery and self-sacrifice, and the love that lays down its life for a friend – even a friend whose name it never knew.'

George W. Bush on 9/11

'The attacks of September 11 were intended to break our spirit. Instead, we have emerged stronger and more unified. We feel renewed devotion to the principles of political, economic, and religious freedom, the rule of law, and respect for human life. We are more determined than ever to live our lives in freedom.'

Rudy Giuliani

We will never forget what hate can destroy and what love can heal. We will never forget it! It felt so strange to be planning for a wedding that week. It was a tangible reminder of what is essential in life. Love. When I awoke on the following morning, Wednesday, September 12th I heard on the radio that Friday the 14th - our wedding day, would be declared a National Day of Mourning. Our honeymoon to New York was cancelled as flights were not flying. The world was grieving with America. While we had a lovely wedding day, the feeling of sadness for all those families stayed with us all. So, we did not throw confetti or blow car horns. Instead, we took our wedding celebrations respectfully and quietly indoors, ever aware and grateful for what we had around us.

As I write this, we are approaching our 20th wedding anniversary. I love Maur today as much as I did back then, but I respect him more. He has been my rock through thick and thin. I will always feel blessed for having his love, respect, support, and friendship. He is a wonderful father, and he was outstanding to my dad who adored him. Maur spent a lot of time with him, and he learned a lot from him and was inspired by him. I loved to see the two of them hang out together. He was like Dad's 5th son.

We have seen lots of happy times in our relationship and some sad times too. We were blessed with two amazing children, a lovely home, good jobs and fantastic friends. Like all couples, we were challenged with sickness, financial strain, and grief. I always tell our kids to be best friends first and marry for love. Looks can go, money can go, but love can stay. It can be cared for. I'm not saying that you can't fall out of love. Some couples do. If you have friendship and love as your foundation, then you have an excellent chance of coping with everything else.

I would not have got through my cancer, Colin's rubella, Mia's asthma, studying as a parent, dad's illness, his death, or my grief, nor could I face my lifelong illness if it wasn't for Maur. I believe that because I was strong and independent when I met Maur, I could be free. I had my career mapped out and many friends, so I didn't need a man, but I wanted him. He was and still is a good man and a true gentleman. That's what I love most about him. I am my best self when I am with him, something that I try not to take for granted.

The poem 'If' by the India-born British Nobel laureate poet Rudyard Kipling is the ultimate inspirational poem that explains how to cope with different situations in life. The poet conveys how to be a good human being. I love to read this poem when I am struggling with a difficult situation. It reminds me of both my dad and my husband. I have shared it with our children and would love to share it with you now.

IF

If you can keep your head when all about you
Are losing theirs and blaming it on you,
If you can trust yourself when all men doubt you,
But make allowance for their doubting too;
If you can wait and not be tired by waiting,
Or being lied about, don't deal in lies,
Or being hated, don't give way to hating,
And yet don't look too good, nor talk too wise:

If you can dream—and not make dreams your master;
If you can think—and not make thoughts your aim;
If you can meet with Triumph and Disaster
And treat those two impostors just the same;
If you can bear to hear the truth you've spoken
Twisted by knaves to make a trap for fools,
Or watch the things you gave your life to, broken,
And stoop and build them up with worn-out tools:

If you can make one heap of all your winnings
And risk it on one turn of pitch-and-toss,
And lose, and start again at your beginnings
And never breathe a word about your loss;
If you can force your heart and nerve and sinew

To serve your turn long after they are gone,
And so hold on when there is nothing in you
Except for the Will, which says to them: 'Hold on!'

If you can talk with crowds and keep your virtue,
Or walk with Kings — nor lose the common touch,
If neither foes nor loving friends can hurt you,
If all men count with you, but none too much;
If you can fill the unforgiving minute
With sixty seconds' worth of distance run,
Yours is the Earth and everything that's in it,
And—which is more—you'll be a Man, my son!

Rudyard Kipling

'You don't need everyone to love you,
just a few good people.'

Charity Barnum. The Greatest Showman

Only you, it has always been, and will forever be,
only you Maur xxx

Thoughts provoked from reading this story

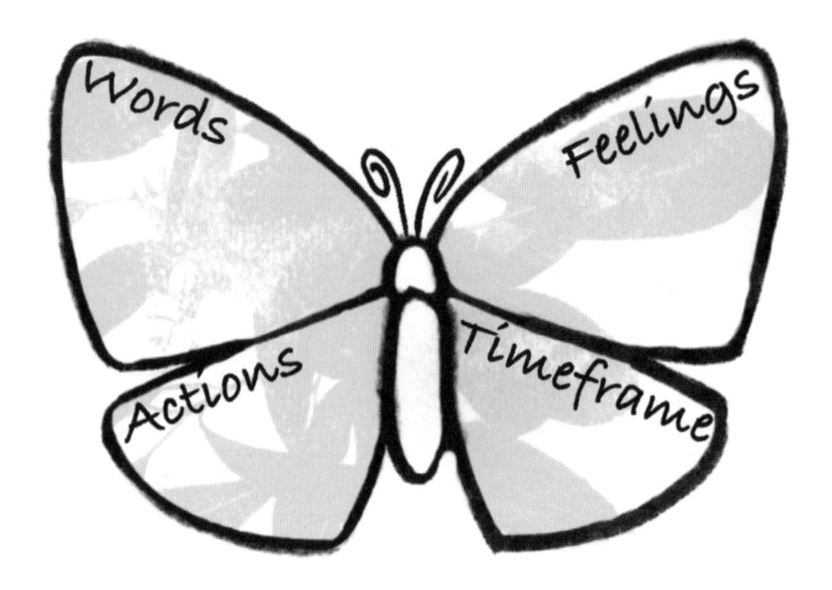

Notes:

Conclusion

I am probably at my happiest right now. I feel strong, both physically and mentally. When I look back on my life to date, I feel pretty emotional. It's been a rollercoaster ride with lots of ups and downs, some screaming, laughter, and dizzy days. If I were to give any advice, it would be this. Keep moving forward. Every day is a new day. Begin again. Be kind.

Life is like the journey of a butterfly. It takes time. It can be ugly at times and then beautiful. Hold hope and gratitude in your heart. I am now at a point in my life where I can look forward without fear. I have been married to my best friend for 20 years, together 27 years. Our two children are now teenagers, and we are nearly there on our mortgage. We may not have it altogether but together we have it all.

During the dark and challenging days, I struggled to see the light at the end of the tunnel. I have learned so much about life, but more importantly, I have learned much about myself. I have begun to listen to what I want and need, which has been very rewarding. I have always used my coping strategies to solve a problem or cope with a challenge, I never thought that these same strategies could turn into a book of hope to raise awareness and fundraise for a cause so deeply rooted in my heart.

I can now focus on my hopes and dreams for the future instead of just firefighting all the time. I can make plans and if they change that's ok. I am delighted to be at a point in my life where I can look forward and move forward with the people I love, healthily and happily.

Sometimes, to move forward, we need to look back at all that we have achieved and all that we have survived. We can each only do our best with what we've got. I have found that writing this book has been very therapeutic for me. I have travelled back and looked at each brick on my road. I have realised that even though there were many difficult roads, the experiences on each one have given me the strength to face the next one. I am so proud to have travelled back to move forward. I can always look at this project with pride. It has been a dream come true.

My next ambition is to write children's books and then a fiction book. I would be complete if I saw my children grow up healthy and happy with fulfilling lives. I will continue to laugh with my friends and loved ones and build more memories. I will continue to work on my inner voice by following the attitude of Judy Judy, looking at facts only. I will do more walking in nature. I would love to build a garden room out the back full of books and sunshine. I'd love to go to New York for my 50th birthday. I will continue with my attitude of gratitude daily check-ins. I hope that I will stay cancer-free, and most importantly, I hope that my husband and children will remain healthy and that we will all live happily ever after.

The end, or as I should say
The beginning.

About the Author

Katherine Dolphin Griffin lives in Ireland. She met her husband at age four and married him twenty two years later. Twenty-seven years on, he's still her prince charming.

Blessed with two amazing teens, Katherine adores her friends and family, especially her beloved late dad, Joe. Katherine is a teacher and enjoys time with her schoolchildren.

Three things that are essential to Katherine;

1. Lover of all things girly, even after coming from a home of all things male.
2. Relishes to chat and lives to write.
3. Believes that laughter is a tonic, communication is a cure and kindness is key.

'When there's no map to guide you, make one and pass it on.'

Katherine Dolphin Griffin

Acknowledgements

There are so many wonderful people in my life. There are many people who have helped and encouraged me either personally or through their books, videos, podcasts or social media on my journey of surviving heartache and rebuilding my life.

My husband and best friend for life, Maur, who always sees the best in me.

My gorgeous children Mia & Colin for making my life complete and for beautifully illustrating my story.

My brothers, for all the memories and the laughs.

My mother, Kay for showing me that love never dies.

My rock, Ger Spring. Also known as, dads best friend, and the one who held my hand.

My in-laws for all their support over the years.

My nieces and nephews, aunts, uncles and cousins.

My dearest forever friends, for the love, trust, support, friendship, loyalty and the joy they bring to my life; Fionnuala O' Riordan, Helena Byrne, Marie Luddy, Anne Fox, Anne Batchelor, Mary Loftus, Deirdre Aherne, Tara Landers, Kay Brandon, Kara

McGregor, Angela Morrissey, Elaine Flavin, Shelly O'Flynn, Caroline McCarthy, Rosie Kane, Sally Clifford, Aisling Lenane, Michelle Cottor, Ruth McCarthy, Ewa Plichta, Niamh Brown, John Taylor, Joanne Murphy and Karen Casey.

My wonderful work colleagues at Midleton Educate Together National School, for all their support and happy days at school.

For all the wonderful school children over the years whom brought me such joy.

My lovely neighbours.

My counsellor Catherina for propping me back upright.

Heather Shields Publishing for supporting my writing journey, editing and formatting my book and teaching me how to self-publish.

Anne Divine, fellow author for her support and encouragement.

Trish Carlos, fellow author for her advice and support.

Peter O'Shea, fellow author for his guidance and support.

Karen Casey, Catherine Casey, Tara Landers, and Angela Humphrey for proofreading my book and for their belief in me, kind words and positivity.

Fionnuala O Riordan for my longest friendship and her endless support.

Marie Luddy for calling me every single day and allowing me the freedom to express my thoughts and emotions without judgement which gave me the confidence to continue with my story.

John Taylor for bringing my 'butterfly thoughts provoking page' to life.

Sally & Jon Waterman, and all at printmybook.com

Thank you to everyone who supported the 2021 Go Fund Me campaign to help with the first print run of this book.

Publicis Dublin for designing the book cover.

Paul Bates for always being at the other end of the phone for all of dads technology questions and for doing the same for me as an IT 'wonky donkey', your help has been invaluable while writing my book and designing my website.

David Keane – Photo on back cover courtesy of The Irish Examiner

Therapy Boutique for the ISBN number and barcode for the book.

Michelle Dorgan, Instagram @printsnpieces for beautifully illustrating my publishing name – Katherine Dolphin Griffin Publishing

Olive O'Sullivan, Instagram @browtiqueIreland and Siobhan Prendiville, @ctc_childrenstherapycentre for all their support every step of the way.

To Professor Seamus O'Reilly, Dr Doran, Dr Sean McCarthy, the staff on St. Theresa's Oncology ward, Mercy Hospital Cork, St James Hospital Dublin, The South Infirmary Victoria University Hospital Cork. The C.U.H and all the staff at Marymount Hospital and Hospice. Thank you for your care, compassion, and professionalism.

Melissa Quilligan for bringing my hair back to life after cancer and to Yaz Sinclair for doing the same with my nails and for doing more than just your jobs.

Last, but not least. My dad, Joe Dolphin, for his love, guidance and his challenge 'be the best that you can be. for me.'

My life is blessed!

Thank You Geraldine Spring

Ger, I want to thank you from the very bottom of my heart for everything that you are and everything that you have done for my family and me. You will never know the extent of my gratitude.

You were a fantastic friend to dad which filled his life with happiness. A friendship built on compassion, trust, equality and honesty. He had such a special place for you in his heart. I have rarely seen anything like your loyalty, support and love.

You have been a rock to me since that day in February 2008 when we sat on either side of dad and learned his fate. Your pragmatic and logical approach helped carry us through the most challenging times in the years that followed. I am privileged to have shared beautiful memories with you and dad, and we are united in those memories forever.

Thank you for propping me up in the days after dad's funeral and continuing to hold me every day since. That kind of love is priceless. Your genuine advice, while appreciating where everyone is coming from, is inviable. You always gave circumstances a chance and gave others the benefit of the doubt showing all of the strength you have inside. You are filled with unique qualities that have brought you this far.

Thank you for everything that you continue to do for me. I am privileged and blessed to call you my friend and I thank Dad every day for bringing you into my life.

Rest In Peace Joe Dolphin. 04/02/17, aged 69 years.

God's Garden

God looked around his garden and found an empty place
He then looked down upon the earth and saw your tired face.
He put his arms around you and lifted you to rest.
With the help of his angels they flew you to
your heavenly place.

God's garden must be beautiful, he always takes the best.
He knew that you were suffering, he knew you were in pain.
He knew that you would never get well on earth again.

He saw the road was getting rough and the hills were hard to climb.
So he closed your weary eyelids and whispered, 'Peace be thine'.
It broke our hearts to lose you but you didn't go alone,
For part of us went with you the day God called you home.

Melissa Shreve

Words Of Wisdom

Most days during my grief I wrote down what I felt or learned that day. They have all helped me. They may help you too.

- Dreams without goals are just dreams. Set goals. I set very small goals.
- Don't identify with another person's point of view unless is makes you a better person.
- Don't react. Wait! Less said is best said. Silence is golden.
- Our perception of reality can change our reality. So wait and think.
- With our words and reactions we can change that reality for others as well. Choose to see sunshine and do not give power to the dark cloud.
- Don't let over critical people drag you down. Their own expectations are probably unreasonable. Maintain your sense of positivity.
- Never accept another person's reality as your own. One must be the most severe judge of oneself.
- We never know another person's true problems or past. What is hidden behind appearances; before we find faults we must work hard to find their best qualities.
- Train the mind to see the good in every situation. No good has ever come out of reacting, think of your circumstances as a test of your spiritual character.

- *When we react we are operating from a low frequency it is important to give ourselves time and space. Breath. Your mind will follow your breath.*
- *Control yourself so that you can navigate the events in your life. When you are thinking negatively and reacting negatively you are quenching your light.*
- *Words are expressed thoughts. Be careful with our words including our words to and thoughts of ourselves.*
- *Faith, hope and love. Your hardest times often lead to your greatest moments in life. Keep going.*
- *Tough situations build strong people in the end*
- *Fix you' by Coldplay - given to me by Maurice after dad died.*
- *Don't confuse movement with progress - movement can be in a circle, progress is moving onwards and upwards.*
- *Plan every day. Failing to plan is planning to fail.*
- *Apply discipline and consistency to your life every day.*
- *That what doesn't kill you makes you stronger.*
- *Energy moves from one thing to another. This is also true with emotional energy. If you are in good mood you pass it on and if you are in bad mood or low energy you can pass it on.*
- *Elephant with diarrhoea - what do you give an elephant with diarrhoea? Plenty of space. If someone is giving you grief and upsetting you, give them plenty of space. Stay away.*
- *Mind over matter - put your mind somewhere else, like on the outcome.*
- *When to go and when to slow? Sometimes you can push yourself to do something, go on that night out with the girls. Sometimes you just need to slow down or stop. Like not going into the staffroom when you are just not able to summon the strength to chat and laugh. Listen to your needs. Nobody knows you better than you.*

- Love yourself - even if it is only about putting on nail varnish or having a nice bath or moisturising or watching tv.
- Surround yourself with positive people. Invest in & nurture friendships.
- JOY - the small word that packs a big punch - joyful people, things, places.
- Belonging.
- Laughter. Best cure. Best preventative. Best medicine.
- Being better than what's thrown at you.
- Apples and oranges - you can't compare, they are different fruits like you are different people. You are not the same. Different upbringing, different education, different beliefs etc.
- Thinking too much about tomorrow while forgetting about today.
- Don't be afraid.
- Short memory/ no memory / please remember. Don't forget who was there for you in the past. Be there for them in the present.
- Different rules for the same behaviour.
- Changing your mindset.
- The long grass - waiting there.
- Teach people how to treat you.
- Smiles and hugs - never underestimate the power of a smile or a hug.
- Our past has a lot to answer for. What we expect from others and what we accept from others.
- What we think we deserve and our ability to go out and get it (or not get it).
- Is what we achieve in life down to circumstances or is it down to our DNA?

- *I do believe that some people can have a real fight on their hands, much bigger than others do. The luck in it is whether or not you have what it takes to get back up every time. Some people are never tested and freak out over the slightest hurdle that they face. I think that I have a good strong grounded grasp of life. I understand what's important and what's not. I think that you get that insight when you face what's important in life head on. You get to know the value of life through seeing the loss and despair that death brings.*
- *The squeaky gate - a squeaky gate will always get oiled. Did you ever notice how that one loud, noisy, person always seems to get listened to, answered, quietened. It's because they are annoying. You just want to quieten them. I say that there is a time and a place for us all to be a squeaky gate. So squeak if you need to.*
- *The high horse. Is he or she on their high horse again?*
- *Moving forward with a heavy heart.*
- *Find your 'somewhere safe' and go there as often as you can. It could be your home, garden, beach, gym.*
- *To know all is to understand all - if we each knew where the other person was coming from, or at least allowed for it, maybe we would understand more.*
- *Try to be understanding, be patient (not always easy) you never know what's going on behind closed doors.*
- *Blessing of the Serenity Prayer - grant me the serenity to accept the things I cannot change, the courage to change the things I can and the wisdom to know the difference.*
- *The green grass. Dad always told me to be aware that the grass may appear greener on the other side. Don't compare yourself, just be yourself. Everybody has their good days and bad days, everything is transient. He also referred to grass when encouraging*

patience. Wait in the long grass. Stay still, be dignified. The wheel goes around. The grass may look greener on the other side. Look and learn but don't obsess. Nobody really knows what goes on in another's patch and we all stem from different foundations. Do the best with your grass. What are you going to do with what you have?

- Carry on - The show must go on - dad would be on the oncology ward and he would have the diary out working away, taking bookings and placing orders. When he was in Marymount, he would send me to the reception to get invoices photocopied. The receptionist was used to copying wills not invoices but the show had to go on for dad. When Dad was receiving his immune booster every three weeks he became very organised with his surroundings and had a nice little 'chemo office' set up in his hospital room. The nurses would come in to change his drip and ask what plug they could plug out to which dad would reply, none. He was gone with the tea trolly for his printer and had something plugged into every available socket. He just got on with it. He got on with life with a smile on his face, a face that did not tolerate pity or doubt.
- The auld kick up the arse - Anyone can get a kick up the arse once, that I can accept but anyone who bends over a second time for a kick deserves the kick he gets. There was an air of unforgiveness about this but I think it's needed in this instance, it's important to assess our heartache, learn from it and move on. If we don't analyse it or learn from it then it's most likely going to happen again.

- *Learn not by mistakes but by example. Some people say that you learn from your mistakes, true somewhat but if we could get most of our learnings from those around us it would be less painful. There are many strong role models in our lives. We are all role models, as parents, grandparents, friends, teachers, employers.*
- *Make a change. To get something you never had you have got to do something you never did.*
- *Mind over matter - put your mind somewhere else, like on the outcome.*
- *JUST DO IT - one step at a time.*
- *Challenges are opportunities - see the opportunity and take it. Doing the same thing over and over and expecting different results? Stop. Review. Change.*
- *PERSISTENCE. If you hang around a barber shop long enough you will get a haircut - you will catch a break.*
- *Have something to fall back on – I would rather have something to fall forward onto. Because I'd like to see what I'm falling on. Every failure is a step closer to success. take risks. Don't quit. Don't fall back.*
- *If you don't fail you're not trying hard enough.*
- *Hard work works.*
- *SUPPORT. 'Like a bridge over troubled water, I will lay me down.'*
- *Busy being busy? Or busy being productive? Just because you're doing a lot more doesn't mean you're getting a lot more done.*
- *Change your mood, you might be surprised.*
- *CREATE SPACE.*
- *THE ART OF DISTRACTION. Keep busy - pull out a cupboard and tidy - it works for me.*
- *THE POWER OF A SMILE. Smile the pain away.*

- *Living your best life?*
- *Laughter - Best cure. Best preventative. Best medicine.*
- *RISE ABOVE. Being better than what's thrown at you.*
- *Don't stoop so low to pick up so little.*
- *Does where you come from play a part in where you r going? How do you work & play. Consider the decisions you make, the people you choose and the people you lose.*
- *Thinking too much about tomorrow while forgetting about today. Don't be afraid.*
- *Remember.*
- *LOVE. Today? Do you love me today? Check in every day with the ones you love.*
- *Love knows no distance.*
- *Smiles and hugs - never underestimate the power of a smile or a hug.*
- *Moving forward with a heavy heart but still moving.*
- *Patience / patient.*
- *The good China - why do we keep it in the press? Why don't we enjoy it every day? Because it will get broken? Isn't life about enjoying the finer things? Why wait for your funeral to get the fine China out? Enjoy your nice things!*
- *A focus. Something to keep you distracted and focused while going through something challenging. Study something interesting. Plan a trip. Decorate. Organise a cupboard or a drawer. Write. I studied through my parents' separation. I worked through their divorce and got promoted several times. I tidied through dad's sickness and wrote through my grief. I decorated through dads death.*

- Set targets for oneself. learn to swim, join the gym and get a sexy body, catch up with old friends or catch a new friend for life. Change your image (hair , clothes or both).
- Journaling. Fill your diary to distract your head and heart - plan a night out, spa break, hike, cycle. Plan an adventure- enter the Galway races.
- Be nice to yourself. Use kind words when you address yourself. Treat yourself with the respect that you give your closest friend.
- You are tough enough - test yourself and you will see.
- Scoring / rating 1-10. - WARNING! Be careful who you give your 10s to. It's a big fall from 10 when they hurt you. I introduced this when I was trying to cope with people following my dad's death. I assigned a rating to people, crazy eh? But it helped. I gave a ten to the most important people and a one to the least important. I had to give a low rating to those who hurt me repeatedly. This reduces the respect you give them in your heart so they are not of value to you and can't hurt you as much. Look at the rating before you deal with the person. I do this all the time especially with the low rates. If I see them approaching me or their name appears on my phone I say to myself this is a two, so don't have huge expectations and say very little, sing Mary had a little lamb in your head while they speak, you will be fine, they are just a two. This is a coping strategy until I learn how to cope with some very difficult people. I am not trying to be mean I am just trying to not take what they say personally when they come to me with their verbal diarrhoea. I am happy to say that now, having used this approach, I am so much better at managing certain people who took from me. Thankfully. I have only a couple of these people left in my life.

- Recovery takes time. See it through.
- Find a sense of purpose - activities which are meaningful to you, involved in community, course, hobby, decorate a room, tidy a room.
- Autonomy. I love this word. It's about a person's ability to act on his or her own values and interests. In order to do these things, the autonomous person must have a sense of self-worth and self-respect.
- Have / create a realistic awareness of self.
- Become adaptable - embrace change, be flexible, optimistic, pragmatic.
- Socially connected – collaboration, support, friends & family.
- Give up self-criticism and demonstrate self-compassion.
- Understand that life is full of challenges - remain open, flexible, willing to adapt and change.
- Mindfulness, health, positive belief in yourself.
- Tenacity - develop problem solving skills.
- Reasoning - anticipate, plan, focus, establish goals.
- Tough situations build strong people.
- Life is a journey of juggling. We are all juggling. I have juggled college life with home (homework over the phone Birmingham to Cork) I have juggled studying for teaching and work, kids, husband, home, dad. I have juggled life and cancer and life and death. It's about building confidence in ourselves
- Smile. A smile breeds a smile.

Frequently Asked Questions

Q. What was it like being the only girl in a house of boys?

A. I loved my family and I knew no different. I loved being an only girl, I always felt included and loved. We had great craic and fantastic memories in our house. The only time that I wished that I had a sister was when dad died.

Q. What was it like juggling home with college?

A. It was busy but fine. I came home as often as I could. I did homework over the phone with my two younger brothers. Dad and the boys were fantastic. They got on with it. We each supported the others dreams.

Q. Did you feel selfish leaving your father and brothers behind in Ireland?

A. Absolutely. I wanted to stay but I knew that I had to be selfish and do what was right for me too. I did my best by them also. I tried anyway.

Q. Did your dad tell you that he loved you?

A. Yes, he had to be trained though, I love the way that over the years he was able to say it more freely. I treasure that now. '*Love you too Kat.*'

Q. What was divorce in 1990s Ireland like?

A. It wasn't seen as a positive thing. There was a stigma that a woman's place was in home. There was no sympathy for the parent who left. There were no concerns about their hurt or the consequences which led to their decision. There was no support for the parent left behind in the home. I felt that we had some kind of contagious disease when we would go to mass on a Saturday night with dad because everyone looked at us with pity, as though we were the unloved children.

Q. Why did you choose to go to college in Birmingham?

A. I chose Birmingham because I loved the course there. It was offering business with tourism. I wanted to have a life away from home too. I wanted to see what it would be like to just be a teenager. It was a terrific decision. I have never regrated it.

Q. Did you and your dad ever fight or fall out?

A. Yes but we couldn't cope if one was 'thick' or 'odd' with the other for more than an hour.

Q. How did you feel about marriage after seeing your parent's divorce?

A. I didn't believe in marriage following my experience with my parents' marriage. However, I loved Maur. instantly and knew that I wanted to be with him forever. We didn't have to marry. We didn't need a certificate or the title of 'married couple'. I think that we married because it was the natural progression in a relationship at the time. Maur had experienced his parent's happy marriage and that gave me hope that we could have one too.

Q. Why leave your job at the bank?

A. I applied for the Bank of Ireland graduate programme, I didn't get it, however, I did get very close to the top of the list. This gave me great confidence in my abilities. I moved on to Eircom. It was definitely the best work decision that I have made. I learned so much, I excelled, I met fantastic people. It was where I learned my worth as an employee.

Q. Where did the confidence with Eircom come from?

A. I wasn't confident. I think that helped because I wasn't arrogant. I was just being myself, chatting and selling on the back of that. There were no secret skills, I took a logical approach. I respected everyone that I worked with and I worked very hard. When I saw the fruits of my labour that's when the confidence came.

Q. Why did you choose to build your house and live next door to your home?

A. I wanted to live in Dublin to be near my job at Eircom and climb the ladder with the company. Maurice hated the thought. I wanted to live near my dad when he got older not when I was at the height of my career. However, we compromised and went for it a little sooner. I am so thankful for listening to Maur because I got to live next to dad and support him in his 9 year cancer battle, something I would not have been able to do if I stayed in Dublin. Dad never got old.

Q. How did you raise the money for a mortgage?

A. We took on extra work – I did interior design and Maurice did car servicing.

Q. Why did you leave Eircom?

A. I wouldn't have been able to sustain working in Dublin and living in Cork. I feel that I wouldn't have been able to give my children the home that I wanted to give them. I didn't want them minded by anyone while I was working. I wanted to be with them as much as I could. I wanted to work. It was and is still very important to me. Teaching would afford me this luxury.

Q. Why did you choose teaching?

A. I love children. I always loved school. I would play school in the garage at home every day when I was a little girl. I wanted to be a teacher however, I didn't get the necessary grade in my Irish paper. I had regrets about that. I blamed mam leaving home before my leaving cert as the reason for not doing as well as I could have. That's not fair. I am in charge of my life and my choices. I am glad that I went back and did my leaving cert again as an adult and achieving what I knew I deserved. I hate having regrets in life. Life is far too short for regrets. Teaching has helped me to learn a lot about children and hence my children have benefited greatly. I love to teach. I love my school.

Q. What was the most difficult part of your teaching journey?
A. The constant juggling and the salary level.

Q. What have been the pros and cons of teaching?
A. The pros have been the ability to do it. The freedom to be at home during all the holidays with my children when they are off school. All the valuable lessons and insights into a child's education. The friends that I've made. The independence that I've gained. The benefits of having my own money. The message that it sends to my daughter that she too can continue to have a career while being a good mother.

The cons have been the intensity of the school day, you don't get the traditional breaks that you would have in other jobs, you are always with the children in your class. Not having free time to myself because when I'm at school the kids are at school and when I'm at home they are at home. All the paper work. The cutbacks from the government.

Q. Are you happy with your decision to teach?
A. Absolutely.

Q. What has been the most painful surgery?
A. The thyroidectomy.

Q. What was the most painful recovery?
A. Thyroidectomy and the gallbladder removal is up there too.

Q. What has/have been the most difficult things to live with?

A. Grief & deafness.

Q. Why don't you give up your job and give yourself time to recover?

A. My medical bills are too high. I have to work full time. I don't have a medical card and my drugs are not on the lifelong illness card (this has not been updated since 1996). I love to work. I am hoping to be able to work part time in a couple of years.

Q. What was the most challenging part of having Cancer and being a mum?

A. The upset that it caused my children and any scars that it may have left them with.

Q. What diagnosis do you struggle with still if any?

Q. My hearing loss. Losing my hearing has been a huge challenge for me, I hate my hearing aids even though I am grateful for the quality of life they give me. I hated being partially deaf in Covid because it's hard to hear people speak with double masking and screens. Most people are patient but I get frustrated with others, especially shops and restaurants where there is a lot of noise and lack of awareness / patience of others.

Q. Did you always want two children or did you want more?
A. I wanted 3. Colin's rubella and night terrors delayed me planning the third then when he turned 4 I was ready but received my cancer diagnosis. I am blessed with two children and I am more than happy. What is for you won't pass you.

Q. What's it like being Coeliac?
A. It's getting easier however coffee shops still have a long way to go. You always have to be prepared when out and about.

Q. How did you end up being prescribed a bowel pace maker?
A. My bowel stopped working. It is in perfect condition so I could keep it but it doesn't work so the bowel pacemaker stimulates the bowl to move and empty.

Q. Why did you have surgery on your womb?
A. In 2018 I experienced significant pain in my womb. My abdomen started to swell and I found it difficult to walk. I went for tests which showed a thickening of the womb lining and the existence of pre-cancerous cells. I also had polyps and fibroids in my womb and endometriosis. I had the lining of my womb removed as well as my fallopian tubes.

Q. What's it like living with life long illness?
A. It's a part time job but I work at it.

Q. What has been the cost of cancer?

A. There have been many. The most significant has been managing and living with the side effects.

Q. Are you glad you did the advert for Vhi Healthcare?

A. Yes. I am proud of how I have created an awareness of cancer and I was proud to be part of their campaign.

Q. Do you believe your dad is helping you?

A. Yes, 100%, every day in every way.

Q. Do you get on with your mother?

A. Yes, my mother is a lovely person and I'm glad to have her in my life.

Q. How is your relationship with brothers?

A. I love my brothers and I would never ever hurt them. We always have each other's back.

Q. What personality traits do you respect & what do you dislike in people?

A. I respect loyalty, open communication and kindness. I dislike controlling personalities, arrogance or ignorance.

Q. Grief now – where are you with it?
A. I am living with it, it's not on top of me it's beside me and that's ok. Grief is the price we pay for love.

Q. What next?
A. I want to write a fiction book and a couple of children's books.

Q. Would you like to retrain again?
A. I'm not sure, I wouldn't mind studying psychology.

Q. what are your hopes for the future?
A. I hope that Mia and Colin graduate from college, get good jobs and are decent happy, healthy adults. I hope that Maur and I experience continued health and happiness together.

Q. Do you speak up?
A. I hate confrontation but yes when I see very wrong doing, especially towards the underdog. I become like a bitch with a bone and I break all of the rules.

Q. Why do you think you are so passionate?
A. It's part of who I am. I am committed and with that comes passion. I value life so if I'm doing something I'm giving it all of me. I don't like unfairness or injustice especially for vulnerable. I like to treat people the way that I expect to be treated.

Q. What puts a smile on your face?

A. I am grateful for all that I have in my life and that puts a smile on my face.

Q. Do you think that you are a good role model for your kids?

A. Yes. I think of my children with every decision that I make. We are very close. I believe that communication is key and trusting their decisions and opinions. I tell them that anything is possible and I tell them that I love them every day. I am completely in awe of the two of them.

Q. What are you most proud of?

A. I am very proud of my husband and kids. I am proud of my kindness and friendships. I am proud of how I get back up every time and make my dreams happen. I am proud of all that I have come through. I am proud of my journey with my dad.

Q. Do you have any regrets?

A. No, because I wrote this book

Q. What have been the highs and lows of writing this book?

A. The highs have been the support and encouragement that I have received and fulfilling a lifelong dream to write. Fulfilling that dream and fundraising for a cause so close to my heart is absolutely mind blowing and humbling. The lows have been the emotional drain from travelling back to those very difficult times that I had to work so hard to drag myself out of. The intensity of the juggling of home, family, full-time job, book and my stamina was also very difficult.

Q. What has been the most challenging part of writing this book?
A. Having to travel back to the sad and painful days. That has been healing too because I am reminded of my love and the strength which that love has given to me.

Q. One piece of advice or a motto what is it?
A. Love, Live, laugh, and hold onto hope in your heart.

Hugs, Katherine

Bibliography

- Education is an admirable thing, but it is well to remember from time to time that nothing that is worth knowing can betaught. - Oscar Wilde
- Change is the law of life. And those who only look to the past or present are certain to miss the future. - J.F. Kennedy
- The price of doing the same old thing is far higher than the price of change. - Bill Clinton.
- Epitaph, posted by David Joyce on Facebook, written by contemporary writer Merrit Malloy. This poem captures how our loved ones can best keep our essence alive after death, not merely through reminiscence but through purposeful acts of love. - Upworthy.com
- You just do it. You force yourself to get up, you force yourself to put one foot in front of the other, and God damn it, you refuse to let it get to you. You fight. You cry. You curse. Then you go about the business of living. That's how I've done it. There's no other way. - Elizabeth Taylor. Not salmon.com
- A tsunami or tidal wave, also known as a seismic sea wave, is a series of waves in a water body caused by the displacement of a large volume of water, generally in an ocean or a large lake. - Wikipedia
- Tsunamis are ranked among the world's most destructive forces. - Britanica.com
- Kind words can be short and easy to speak, but the echoes are truly endless. - Mother Teresa, Inc.com

- *Words have energy and power and the ability to help, to heal, to hinder, to hurt, to harm, to humiliate, and to humble. - Yehunda Berg, inc.com*
- *I've often suffered from imposter syndrome. Imposter syndrome (IS) refers to an internal experience of believing that you are not as competent as others perceive you to be. While this definition is usually narrowly applied to intelligence and achievement, it links perfectionism and the social context. - verywellmind.com*
- *Raise your words, not your voice. It's the rain that grows flowers, not the thunder. - Rumi Inc.com*
- *The very things that hold you down are going to lift you. - Timothy Mouse, Dumbo. Popsugar.*
- *Vulnerability is not the opposite of resilience. Vulnerability builds resilience. Projecting perfection protects your ego but shuts people out and stunts your growth. Revealing struggles shows humility and humanity, opening the door to new sources of support and strength. - @adamgrant on @mattzhaig's stories on Instagram.*
- *The three C's of life - choices, chances, and changes. Choose to take a chance if you want anything in life to change. - Maria Gleason CBT, Maria Gleason.com*
- *Too many people are thinking of security instead of opportunity. They seem to be more afraid of life than death. - James F. Byrnes, positivityblog.com*
- *The only thing we have to fear is fear itself. - Franklin D Roosevelt.*
- *Curiosity will conquer fear even more than bravery will. - James Stephens, positivityblog.com*
- *When we are no longer able to change a situation, we are challenged to change ourselves. - Victor Frankl.*

- *Understanding is the first step to acceptance, and only with acceptance can there be recovery. - J K Rowling Harry Potter and the goblet of fire*
- *For, after all, the best thing one can do when it's raining is to let it rain. - Henry Wadsworth Longfellow, Brainy reads*
- *Stop All the Clocks by W.H. Auden, read in the movie four weddings and a funeral.*
- *Fall on me – sung by Andrea and Mateo Boccelli*
- *We cannot, after all, judge a biography by its length, by the number of pages in it. We must judge it by the richness of the contents - sometimes the 'unfinished' are among the most beautiful symphonies. - Victor Frankl.*
- *It doesn't matter to the sun - song lyrics by Rosie Thomas.*
- *I have not failed. I've just found 10,000 ways that won't work. - Thomas Edison*
- *Fix You song lyrics– Coldplay*
- *The problem is not the problem. The problem is your attitude about the problem. - Jack Sparrow, Pirates of the Caribbean, storiesinc.com*
- *Believe you can, then you will. - Mulan, princess storiesinc.com*
- *The greatest discovery of all time is that a person can change his future by merely changing his attitude. - Oprah Winfrey, country living.com.*
- *Be the change you want to see in the world. - Mahatma Gandhi, country living.com*
- *How to Avoid toxic Positivity. @avamariedoodles Instagram.*
- *I learned long ago, never to wrestle with a pig. You get dirty, and besides, the pig likes it. - George Bernard Shaw*
- *Poem - A people place by William J. Crocker*

- *I am thankful to all who have said no to me, and it is because of them that I am doing it myself. - Albert Einstein - wisdom quotes.com*
- *The way I see it if you want to see the rainbow, you got to put up with the rain. - Dolly Parton - Berries.com*
- *Don't be afraid to give up the good to go for the great. - John D. Rockefeller, country living.com*
- *Letting go of the judgment and the negativity makes space for love and kindness and a passion for everything around you and what you do. - Holly Willoughby.*
- *For to be free is not merely to cast off one's chains, but to live in a way that respects and enhances the freedom of others. - Nelson Mandela, success.com*
- *The most courageous act is still to think for yourself. Aloud. - Coco Chanel, Classy.org*
- *Be yourself; everyone else is already taken. - Oscar Wilde*
- *Be who you are and say what you feel. Because those who mind don't matter, and those who matter don't mind. - Bernard M. Maruch*
- *Dr. Clodagh @thewellnesspsychologist. Instagram.*
- *Niamh Connolly @TransformCBT. Instagram.*
- *Micro-steps Podcast by Arianna Huffington.*
- *@ehopkins, therapy coach. Instagram.*
- *TikTok video by @iamqueenskye; We think we have time. Time is free, but it is priceless. You cannot own it, but you can use it. You can't keep it, but you can spend it, and once it's gone, you can never get it back.*

- *Look after your physical, emotional, mental, and spiritual health and wellbeing. If you don't value yourself, nobody else will. - Anne Devine, Encourage yourself, encourage others*
- *Be a strong woman so your daughter will have a role model, and your son will know what to look for in a woman when he's a man. - Motivational quotes for women – small bus-trends*
- *There is no force more powerful than a woman determined to rise. – Bosa Sebele, Ponwell.com*
- *Bring your talent into the open. Embrace it and celebrate it. Share it with others. - Anne Devine, Encourage yourself, encourage others.*
- *Happiness is a state of mind. It's just in accordance to how you look at things. - Walt Disney*
- *Albert Einstein said, There are only two ways to live your life. One is as though nothing is a miracle. The other is as though everything is a miracle.*
- *We tend to forget that happiness doesn't come as a result of getting something we don't have, but rather of recognizing and appreciating what we do have. - Frederick Keonig*
- *What is real happiness? She answered, Happiness is not fulfilling every pleasure or getting every outcome you desire. Happiness is being able to enjoy life with a peaceful mind that is not constantly craving for more. It is the inner peace that comes with embracing change. - Yung Pueblo*
- *We can only learn to love by loving - Rumi, Pinterest*
- *All of me loves all of you - John Legend*
- *Never doubt that I love - William Shakespeare*

- *It's also a memory of bravery and self-sacrifice, and the love that lays down its life for a friend – even a friend whose name it never knew.* - George W. Bush on 911.
- *The attacks of September 11 were intended to break our spirit. Instead, we have emerged stronger and more unified. We feel renewed devotion to the principles of political, economic, and religious freedom, the rule of law, and respect for human life. We are more determined than ever to live our lives in freedom.* Rudy Giuliani, Success.com

- Poem - IF – by Rudyard Kipling.
- *Owning our own story and loving ourselves through that process, is the bravest thing that we will ever do.'* Brené Brown
- *'People talk about caterpillars becoming butterflies as though they just go into a cocoon, slap on wings, and are good to go. Caterpillars have to dissolve into a disgusting pile of goo to become butterflies. So if you're a mess wrapped up in a blanket right now, keep going.'* Eileen Hopkins, Jennifer Wright, @ ehopkinstherapycoach
- *Sometimes I feel lost,' said the boy. 'Me too,' said the Mole, 'but we love you, and love brings you home. I think everyone is just trying to get home,' said the Mole.* The Boy, the Mole, the Fox, and the Horse. Charlie Mackesy.
- *'Butterflies show us how we can go within ourselves to dissolve old forms and morph, rebuilding and evolving ourselves, they show us the importance of surrender and trust as part of the essential process of growth and renewal.' - Anna Cariad-Barrett Eco* therapist and co-author of *Sacred Medicine of Bee, Butterfly, Earthworm, and Spider*

- *'We can do no great things, only small things with great love.'* - Mother Theresa
- Poem - *A people place by William J. Crocker*
- *'Letting go of the judgment and the negativity makes space for love and kindness and a passion for everything around you and what you do.'* - Holly Willoughby
- *'What do you want to be when you grow up?' 'Kind,'* said the boy. - Charlie Mackesy. The boy, the mole, the fox, and the horse.
- *'You don't need everyone to love you, just a few good people.'* - Charity Barnum. The Greatest Showman
- *'Grief is like a wound that needs attention to heal. We try to face our feelings openly and honestly, express or release our emotions fully, and tolerate and accept our feelings for however long it takes for the wound to heal. Therefore, it takes great courage to grieve.'* - The Courage to Grieve. Judy Tatelbaum

Story Theme Highlights

Story 1: Home Sweet Home

He was my first call in the morning and my last call at night.

Story 2: Nothing to fear, but fear itself

One step at a time. The mountain gets smaller with every bucket of soil that you remove from it.

Story 3: Help

When you are lost, nothing looks familiar. Everything is out of position.

Story 4: Change our words, change our mindset

Be your cheerleader.

Story 5: finding your voice

Your point of view matters because you matter.

Story 6: Building resilience

When life throws you a curveball, you can choose to either duck, get hit, or swing.

Story 7: Your own worst enemy

It's important to celebrate small successes

Story 8: Accepting the things we cannot change

The most challenging times often lead to the most incredible moments

Story 9: Perseverance, finding a way to cope
Extraordinary people have come into my life many times on my journey

Story 10: Stuck in reverse
My Dad's heart was slowing, and mine was breaking

Story 11: Positivity and being real
'I learned long ago, never to wrestle with a pig. You get dirty, and besides, the pig likes it.'
George Bernard Shaw

Story 12: When it is s**t, say its s**t
'You cannot control the behaviour of others, but you can control how you react to it and cope with it.'

Story Thirteen: Changing what we can
We think we have time
'Time is free, but it is priceless. You cannot own it, but you can use it. You can't keep it, but you can spend it, and once it's gone, you can never get it back.'

Story 14: Working Woman
Maybe it's about talking a bit of sense into yourself.

Story 15: Happiness
Happiness is that feeling that comes over you when you know life is good, and you can't help but smile.

Story 16: To have and to hold
Little did I know that I was sitting and playing a few meters away from my future husband.